NELLIE BLY, Reporter

By NINA BROWN BAKER

Illustrated by Wayne Blickenstaff

SCHOLASTIC BOOK SERVICES

Published by Scholastic Book Services, a division
of Scholastic Magazines, Inc., New York, N.Y.

Copyright © 1956, by Nina Brown Baker. This edition is published by Scholastic Book Services, a division of Scholastic Magazines, Inc., by arrangement with Henry Holt and Company.

5th printing .... March 1969

Printed in the U.S.A.

Contents

1 "And Have a Little Song"   1

2 What Girls Are Good For   10

3 The Girl Reporter   20

4 No Girls Wanted   31

5 The Great Mr. Pulitzer   43

6 Behind Asylum Bars   53

7 Watch Out for Nellie Bly   65

8 The Big Idea   75

9 Around the World   87

10 Seeing Nellie Home   98

11 Gold and Glory   107

12 The Ending Is Sad   113

1 "And Have a Little Song"

Mrs. Cochrane! Where in the world is Lizzie? The crowd's all over at my house, waiting for her. Doesn't she know what time it is?"

"I expect not." Lizzie's mother swung open the front door, letting in a blast of icy winter air. "Come on in, Madge, before you freeze us out. She's been up in her room ever since supper. You know how she is when she gets at her writing. Seems like she loses all track of time."

1

Madge moved toward the staircase, her feet in heavy galoshes clattering over the bare floor.

"Her writing!" she repeated scornfully. "How she can waste her time over such stuff! She *knew* we are going skating at Round Pond tonight. Really, there are times when I lose all patience with her!"

Mrs. Cochrane smiled. She was a plump, comfortable little woman, with scarcely a wrinkle on her placid face.

"It's no use losing patience with Lizzie," she said mildly. "She'll do what she wants to do, and there's no stopping her. But I know she meant to go to the skating party. I guess she just forgot."

"Well, I'll go rout her out. I only hope I can make her hurry."

"That's more than I've ever been able to do," Lizzie's mother said cheerfully. "But go ahead and try. You know where her room is—the first door at the top of the stairs."

Madge clumped up the steps. The hallway was warm from the big coal-burning stove in the living room. But when she threw open Lizzie's door, a chill breath greeted her.

It was a plain little room, skimpily furnished in golden oak. The only chairs were a little willow rocker and an unpainted kitchen stool, which had been a chair, too, until it lost its back.

Lizzie had drawn the stool up to the marble-topped

washstand. There she sat, with her back to the door. Crumpled paper lay all about her. She was scribbling furiously by the light of an oil lamp. She did not look up when Madge called her name.

"Lizzie!" the visitor repeated. Still no answer.

Madge plunged forward. She was a big, awkward girl, and the light was dim. Before she knew it, she had tripped over the washbowl and pitcher at Lizzie's feet.

The clatter of china did what the voice had failed to do. Lizzie turned, rubbing her eyes with inky fingers.

"Madge! Do you have to fall into the room like that? You might have broken Mama's second-best set."

"I might have broken my neck, too," Madge said crossly. "What's this stuff doing on the floor, anyway? It belongs on the washstand."

"I know. But I had to have room to write. Oh, Madge, you're just in time. Let me read you this. I've spent hours over it, but I think I've got it at last. Do sit down and listen."

She waved toward the rocking chair, but Madge shook her head.

"No, thanks. I didn't come to listen to poetry. Do you——?"

"But it's not poetry this time. And it's not a made-up story, either. It's a letter to a newspaper—an answer to that perfectly horrible editorial in the *Dispatch*. 'What Girls Are Good For' indeed! I've been boiling mad ever since it came out. And every time I read it over I get more furious."

"Then what do you read it for?" Madge asked reasonably. "There's nothing on the editorial page but politics and stuff anyway. I always skip over it and turn to fashions and society. That's all there is in the paper that's any use to girls."

"Now you sound just like this hateful old editor, Madge. That's what *he* thinks. All that girls are good for is to get dressed up and look pretty. And catch a husband if they can. Then they must spend their lives making him comfortable and happy. We're good enough for that, but we're not good enough for jobs of our own."

"Well, *I'd* rather have a husband than a job," Madge said simply. "Any girl would."

"Oh, *Madge!* You don't even know when you're being insulted. For it's an insult to all of us, what he says. Just listen." She picked up a clipping. " 'The growing employment of women in business establishments is a grave threat to our national welfare. They displace men who should be the family wage earners. With their inferior brains, they muddle every transaction entrusted to them and —' "

"Lizzie!" Madge's voice was the stronger, and she raised it to drown out the reading. "I will not listen! Getting all worked up about a silly old newspaper article! You just stop now, before I take it away from you and tear it up."

"Well, all right. Don't listen to that horrible old man then. But listen to me. Here's what I've written to him. And if this doesn't blister him, nothing will."

"Blister him if you must. You're not going to blister me," Madge said firmly. "No, I won't hear it. Not a word of it. Look, Lizzie, I've had enough of your foolishness. Are you going skating tonight or aren't you? Because if you're not, just say so, and we'll go on without you."

"Skating? Good heavens, was it tonight? I'd forgotten completely. What time is it anyway?"

"Just about an hour late, that's all. And you in your wrapper and curl papers! I suppose it'll take you another hour to dress. Really, Lizzie, you're too provoking."

Lizzie shuffled the pages together. "I'm not sure about my last paragraph," she said thoughtfully. "Oh, well, it'll do, I guess. Just wait until I address the envelope. We can drop it at the post office as we go by. Now don't fuss, Madge. I'll be ready in no time. Sit down and make yourself comfortable."

"Comfortable!" Madge snorted. "It's cold as the tomb in here. Aren't you freezing?"

Lizzie glanced toward the small heating stove.

"Oh, yes, the fire went out. That's why I'm wearing

my flannel wrapper. It was easier than building it up again."

She threw off the swaddling wrapper and smiled.

"There, you see? I *am* dressed, even to my shoes. I only have to do my hair. . . . Madge, do you think he'll print my letter?"

"I don't know, and I don't care. For pity's sakes, Lizzie, hurry!"

"I can't, and you know it," Lizzie said reproachfully. "I haven't been putting my hair up long enough to get the hang of it yet. It was so much easier when I wore it in a braid. Being grown up has its drawbacks, I find."

She moved over to the dresser. With unskilled hands she twisted her heavy dark hair into a shaky bun. She pulled the paper curlers from her thick bangs and combed them out into a fashionable fringe.

"I hope it stays up," she said doubtfully.

"Never mind, your fascinator will cover it," her friend answered.

Madge took the crocheted head scarf and thick wool coat from the closet. "Where are your overshoes? And your skates? Downstairs? Oh, my goodness, Lizzie, your fingers! They're all over ink. Is there hot water in the kitchen?"

"I expect not, if Mama's done the supper dishes. But I'll keep my mittens on. Where's my letter? Oh, here it is. Well, come on, Madge. I thought you were in such a hurry."

Madge's house was a few doors down the street. In front of it stood a farm wagon whose wheels had been replaced by sled runners. The wagon box was filled with hay, covered with old bed quilts.

Madge gave a vigorous tug to the string of sleigh bells which hung from the horses' harness. A cheerful chime rang out on the frosty air.

At the sound the house door opened and a crowd of boys and girls surged out. They were well wrapped against the winter's cold, with skates slung over their shoulders.

"Lizzie's here," Madge called in her hearty voice. "Get in, everybody. We're ready to start."

They piled into the wagon, settling themselves in the hay, pulling the covers over their laps. The old farmer on the wagon seat clucked to the horses, and the clumsy vehicle moved off. The sleigh bells tinkled merrily. The runners squeaked over the firm-packed snow.

Lizzie leaned forward to touch the driver's shoulder.

"Stop at the post office, Mr. Jim, please. I have a letter to mail."

"Was that what kept you so long, writing a letter?" one of the boys asked. "Must have been a love letter, if it took all that time."

Lizzie laughed. "It was a long way from a love letter,

Joe. About as far away as you can get. I gave that scoundrel a piece of my mind that ought to make him squirm."

"What scoundrel?" asked the boy. But Madge broke in impatiently.

"Oh, Joe, don't get her started. She's mad about something she read in the *Dispatch,* and she wrote the editor to tell him so. That's all there is to it. I don't want to hear any more about it. Nobody but Lizzie would get excited about a piece in the paper."

"Well, everybody ought to," Lizzie began indignantly. "Every girl ought to, anyway. I suppose you boys would agree with that awful old man. Why, do you know what he said?"

"We—do—not—want—to—know!" Madge shouted. "There, that's the last of that. We're supposed to be out for a good time. I'll tell you; let's start a song, Come on now, everybody:

"'*Nellie Bly, Nellie Bly, bring the broom along*
  We'll sweep the kitchen clean, my dear, and
    have a little song.
  Poke the wood, my lady love, and make the fire
    burn,
  And while I take the banjo down, just give the
    mush a turn.'"

It was a favorite Stephen Foster melody, and one by one they all joined in.

Lizzie sat in offended silence through the first verse, but the catchy tune was too much for her. She flashed a forgiving smile at Madge and lifted her clear, true contralto in the rollicking chorus;

" 'Heigh, Nellie, Ho, Nellie, listen, love, to me;
I'll sing for you, play for you, a dulcet melody.' "

2   *What Girls Are Good For*

It was one week later. The dull light of a January day struggled through the grimy office windows. The shabby old building shook with the thunder of presses. George Madden, editor of the Pittsburgh *Dispatch*, sat alone in his cubbyhole of a private office, bent over a pile of copy paper.

He looked up with a scowl as the office boy stood in the doorway.

"Well, what is it now?" he snapped.

"Lady to see you, boss. She says you sent for her," the boy added hastily as Madden's frown deepened. "Here's her card."

The editor took the card, daintily engraved in fine Spencerian script. "Miss Elizabeth Cochrane."

"I've got no time for her now," he said shortly. "Tell her to go away."

"But I can't go away until I've seen you, Mr. Madden." A meek little voice spoke from behind the office boy. "Because you asked me to come."

Gently but very firmly she pushed the boy aside and stepped into the room.

She had dressed with great care. The brown cashmere with its fluted deep flounce was her Sunday best. She had borrowed Mama's short sealskin jacket, and set the matching fur cap carefully atop her frizzed brown bangs. The high-button shoes were polished to a mirror shine. Her dress collar was outlined with fresh white ruching. Her cheeks were pink with excitement, and her hazel eyes sparkled. Altogether she looked very young, and distractingly pretty.

George Madden pushed back his eyeshade and looked at her in amazement.

"There must be some mistake, Miss. What makes you think I wanted to see you?"

"This." With a hand that shook a little, she held

out a letter. "You are Mr. Madden, aren't you, sir? You wrote this letter."

He glanced at it briefly. "I wrote it to some female crank who sent me a most abusive letter. So abusive that I could have her arrested for it. I may do it too," he added grimly. "I suppose she was afraid to face me. Well, you go back and tell her, child, that all I had in mind was to give her a good dressing-down. And I'm still going to do it, if she has the nerve to show up at this office. If not——"

Lizzie's shaking legs would not hold her up. Without being asked, she sank into a chair beside the desk. But she forced her voice to steadiness.

"Mr. Madden, it may be that I expressed myself in unladylike terms. I was very angry over your editorial. I answered you while my anger was at white heat. If you feel that I deserve arrest, you must have me arrested. Or if you want to give me 'a good dressing-down,' I am here to receive it. But whatever you do, I shall still feel the same way about your article. It was— *abominable*, sir!"

"Well, well, a kitten with claws!" The editor stared at her. "Let me get this straight. *You* wrote that letter?"

"Yes, Mr. Madden. And I'm sorry if I hurt your feelings."

In spite of herself, her voice faltered. He looked very big and fierce and angry. Could he really send her to jail for what she had written? It was a frightened child's face that she raised to his.

"What—what are you going to do to me?" she quavered.

His hard glare softened a bit.

"Come now, young lady, I won't eat you, you know. Let's be sensible about this. I wrote an editorial, 'What Girls Are Good For.' I take it you think I was wrong."

New anger brought back Lizzie's courage.

"I *know* you were wrong!" she flashed. "It's not fair to say we muddle everything we touch, because our brains are inferior. There have been women who did men's jobs, and did them better than men could!"

"Yes? Maybe you can name some."

"Certainly I can! Queen Elizabeth, and Joan of Arc, and—oh, I can't think of all the names. There were lots of them. And there'd be more if you men just gave us a chance. How can we use our brains if you won't give us the jobs to try? Some women are bird-brained, as you said. But so are some men. Didn't you ever have any bird-brained *men* working for you, Mr. Madden? Oh, I'm sorry," she gasped. "I didn't mean to be rude. I'm afraid I let my tongue run away with me."

"As girls' tongues do," he said dryly. But he did not sound so cross now. His keen eyes studied her flushed face for a minute. Then he seemed to make up his mind.

"Listen to me, young lady. Your letter was not an answer to my article. You didn't try to show that I was wrong. All you did was to scold me for what I said. Calling names doesn't prove anything. You say women's brains are as good as men's. All right. I'm going to give you a chance to prove that. Pull your chair up to the desk. Right there, across from me."

Wonderingly she obeyed.

"Here's pencil and paper," he went on. "I want *you* to write an article on 'What Girls Are Good For.' Newspaper writing is a man's job. Let's see how that female brain of yours handles it. Or would you prefer not to put it to the test? I can't make you try, if you'd rather not."

"Of course I'll try." She sounded scared but determined. "And—you were right, Mr. Madden. Calling names doesn't prove anything. I'll try to do better this time."

He nodded and went back to his own work, seeming to forget that she was there.

She took up the pencil and looked blankly at the paper before her. At first the words would not come. But names came crowding into her mind. The names of women who had done a man's work in the world. Queen Elizabeth I, Joan of Arc, Molly Pitcher—she tried to give a brief sketch of each. Florence Nightingale, yes, and Mother Bickerdyke, who defied doctors and generals to nurse the soldiers of our own Civil

War. Dorothea Dix, who forced the states to set up hospitals for the hopelessly insane. Then there were the women writers—Harriet Beecher Stowe and Elizabeth Barrett Browning and a host of others. And Rosa Bonheur, the painter. And—and——

Her pencil flew across the paper. She forgot the silent man opposite her. She did not hear the office noises or notice when the presses fell silent. Page after scribbled page joined the growing pile at her elbow. At last she added the final sheet and looked up.

Mr. Madden had finished his own work and was tilted back in his chair, glancing through the latest edition of the *Dispatch*.

"Please, I've finished now," Lizzie said timidly. "I'll just look it over for corrections."

He brought his chair legs down to the floor and reached out his big hand.

"I'll attend to the corrections. You put your heart into your writing, young woman, I'll say that for you. Much too much of it, of course. But let's see."

He picked up a blue pencil and attacked the manuscript. Lizzie's heart sank as she watched the pencil ruthlessly strike out words, sentences, and paragraphs. But he went through to the end. Then, without speaking, he fished a crumpled five-dollar bill from his pocket and pushed it toward her.

"For me?" she asked incredulously.

"Certainly. The *Dispatch* pays for what it prints.

This will appear in the Sunday edition, if you want to watch for it."

"You're going to *print* it?" she gasped.

She would not have believed his grim face could look so kindly as it did when he smiled. He smiled now, and Lizzie's own anxious face relaxed.

"It's good, young lady. It's d— Um. Mustn't say the big D before ladies. I suppose your daddy never swears?"

"My daddy is dead, Mr. Madden. But I did hear him swear once, when a big lawbook fell on his toe. He was a judge, you know."

"No, I didn't know. Tell me about your family, Miss Cochrane."

Lizzie sighed. She would much rather talk about her article, and hear what Mr. Madden had started to say. Big D *good*—wasn't that what he had meant? But a lady must always be polite.

"I have a mother and brothers, Mr. Madden," she began obediently. "We moved to Pittsburgh last year, right after Daddy died. My brothers are in business here, and they thought Mama and I should be near them. We don't live with them though. We have a little house out by the park. I finished high school last year, and, well, I guess that's all there is to tell."

"You're out of school then. How old are you?"

Lizzie hesitated. Did a girl have to be of age before her work could be printed in the paper?

"I'm practically eighteen," she said firmly.

" 'Practically' doesn't mean anything. When were you born, and where?"

There was no use trying to keep anything from him.

"May 7, 1867," she answered. "And we lived at Cochrane's Mills, in Armstrong County. It's just a little place—my grandfather started it with a mill there. But Daddy sold the mill when he got elected judge. He was the best judge they ever had," she said proudly. "And he let me read his lawbooks and listen to trials. He said I'd make a good lawyer myself if—if——"

"If you hadn't been a girl," the editor finished for her.

Lizzie's chin went up. "That wasn't what he said, Mr. Madden. He said I'd make a good lawyer, if only people weren't so prejudiced against women lawyers. Even so, I think he would have let me study law if he'd lived. But my brothers don't approve of it."

"I bet they don't. Tell me, how are your brothers going to feel about your appearing in print?"

A stricken look crossed Lizzie's face.

"They won't like it at all," she admitted. "They feel as you do; that a girl's only job is to catch a husband. They're always asking if I haven't found a fellow yet. It makes me so *mad!*"

The editor's smile broadened. "And you haven't found one then? Don't you ever intend to marry?"

"Of course I do, someday. But not for years and

years. The world is so big and so wonderful, and I've seen so little of it. I want to see it all. I want to do great things and know people who are doing great things. I want—oh, Mama says I don't know what I want, and I suppose she's right. I guess I just want wonderful things to happen to me. Do you think that's being crazy, Mr. Madden?"

He shook his head. "No, I think it's just being young. When we're seventeen, we all want wonderful things to happen to us. Well, let's hope your dreams come true, child. Now about your brothers. You're not eighteen yet, so I suppose they have some authority over you. If they think your name shouldn't appear in print——"

"Then you can't print it?" Quick tears started to Lizzie's eyes. "Oh, I knew it was too marvelous to be true!"

"Now, now, hold your horses, young lady. Your article is d— extremely good, and I certainly mean to print it. And others, if you'll write them for us. Do you have ideas for any more?"

"I could think of dozens," she said eagerly. "But it's no use, if the boys won't let you print them."

"The boys won't object to your earning a little extra money, surely," he pointed out.

"Mama and I don't depend on them for money," she explained. "Daddy left us enough to live on if we're very, very careful. It's seeing the family name in print they won't like. They'll say it's not ladylike. Or their wives will," she added.

"Well, there's a way around that. We'll simply use a pseudonym. A pen name," he explained, as she looked bewildered at the unfamiliar word.

Lizzie's face brightened. "Oh, of course! Why didn't I think of that? I—now what shall I call myself?"

"It's for you to choose. I suppose you'll pick something fancy—Gwendolyn Araminta Montmorency or something of the sort."

Lizzie shook her head. "No. It must be short and easy to remember, and—well, businesslike." She thought a minute, and the words of a song sounded in her ears.

"Nellie Bly—would that do? It's short and simple, and people already know if from the song. That will help them to remember it."

"Nellie Bly. Nellie Bly." The editor tried it over. "Yes, it's a good choice. Can't be misspelled, or mispronounced, and it'll stick in their minds from one article to the next. Here." He pushed the last page of her manuscript toward her. "Sign it with your new name."

She wrote it out carefully in her neat, clear handwriting. No one could have guessed how often she was to sign that name, nor what fame and fortune would come her way under it.

3 The Girl Reporter

Lizzie was ecstatically happy as she left the *Dispatch* office. Her happiness faded quickly when she reached home.

Her brother Albert and his wife had come to supper. They received her great news with a chilling dash of cold water.

"Most unsuitable," the sister-in-law said primly. "A newspaper office is no fit place for a young lady.

All those rough men, smoking and chewing tobacco. And the language they use! Oh, no, it won't do at all. You must put your foot down, Mother Cochrane. Tell her we can't have it."

Mama's kind face looked anxious. If it had been left to her, Lizzie knew, there would be no trouble. Oh, why did relatives always think they had to interfere in your life?

"Mama knows a lady can be a lady wherever she is," she said hotly. "And besides, I'm not going to work at the *Dispatch* office. Even Mr. Madden says that wouldn't do, although I can't see why. I am to write my articles at home and take them in once a week. Mama can't object to that. Can you, dear?"

"Well, I don't—" the elder Mrs. Cochrane began uncertainly. But Brother Albert's deep voice drowned her out.

"*I* can object, and I do. No sister of mine is going to make a public spectacle of herself. There are only three occasions on which a lady's name should be mentioned in the newspapers. When she is born, when she marries, and when she dies. Any book of etiquette will tell you so," he finished triumphantly.

Lizzie sighed. It was quite true. The etiquette books did say just that. A true lady saw to it that she never "made herself conspicuous" by newspaper mention. The notion was already becoming a little old-fashioned, but Brother Albert held old-fashioned views. So did his wife.

"Dragging the family name in the dust!" Mrs. Albert snorted. "I wonder that you have the gall to face us with such a disgraceful scheme. Well, we're all agreed that we can't have it. Mother, you tell her so."

For Mama's sake Lizzie held down her rising anger. As gently as she could she said, "But I'm not going to use my real name. I'll sign myself Nellie Bly. Nobody will know it's me."

"A pretty idea," her brother sneered. "Hiding under a false name, like a criminal. Well, that proves it. Even you are ashamed of what you're proposing to do. You don't dare do it under your own name."

"But—but—" Lizzie began helplessly. How could he be so unreasonable? She would have been proud to sign her own name. It was only consideration for her family's feelings that made her adopt a false one. Couldn't he see that?

She tried to make him see it, with no success. The bitter family quarrel went on and on, until finally Mama put a stop to it.

"Now you children can just quit wrangling," she said with unexpected firmness. "There's no harm in Lizzie writing pieces for the paper, if she writes them here at home. If you think she shouldn't take them to the newspaper office by herself, I can go with her. Nobody's going to know that our Lizzie is Nellie Bly unless we tell them. I don't see what the fuss is all about. Seems to me we ought to be proud of our little girl, instead of picking at her. Who would have thought she could write something good enough to be printed? Now let's stop this silly squabbling and have some supper."

It was not often that the gentle mother took a stand. When she did, there was no moving her. Thankfully Lizzie sprang up to set the table. She knew that the matter of her job was settled.

It was settled, but not very satisfactorily. Albert and his wife never ceased to find fault. The other brothers, when they heard, were equally disapproving. It was generally felt that Lizzie was disgracing the family name.

There were some grounds for their disapproval. The plan of little pieces written at home did not work out. Lizzie had argued that girls are fit to do men's work if they could get the jobs. She knew that girls *were* working, in stores and factories, and even in some offices. She started a series of articles to show how that work was being done.

She could not find out by sitting at home. She had to go into the stores and factories and see for herself. She was bound to run into people who recognized her as the Cochrane girl. That she called herself Nellie Bly did not fool her brothers' business friends.

She was too absorbed in her new work to mind the family criticism. What she saw in the factories horrified her. She lost interest in proving how well women could replace men in industry. Instead, she set herself to expose the frightful conditions under which they did it. Long hours, cold and dirty quarters, starvation wages—with glowing indignation she made the *Dispatch* readers see what she saw.

Her articles were not cheerful reading. But the paper's circulation boomed. Nellie Bly spared no one, no matter how rich or important. Factory owners fumed and wrote furious letters to the editor. But Nellie was scrupulously fair. When she found a place where women workers were well treated, she made a story out of that. Soon the worst of them began to see that it was good business to improve conditions and earn a favorable write-up.

Mr. Madden was delighted with his enterprising girl reporter. Responsible businessmen commended her. The decent, fair-minded public wrote letters of praise. But their sister's modest fame did not win over the Cochrane brothers. They nagged at her constantly. And what was worse, they made their mother's life miserable.

Nellie did not mind for herself. It disturbed her that poor Mama must bear the brunt of their scoldings. She had no intention of giving up her newspaper work, but after nearly a year of it she came to Mr. Madden with a new plan.

"I want you to send me to Mexico," she told him. "A lot of Americans are going there to work on the railroads and in the mines. Just last week President Porfirio Díaz sent out a call for Pennsylvania miners. He offers high wages, but who knows what the living would be like? Before a man takes his family down there, he needs to know about housing and schools and food—everything! I'll go find out and tell our readers."

Mr. Madden looked doubtful. He knew, as everyone knew, how President Díaz was trying to modernize his backward country. Railroads were being built and mines opened up faster than Mexican laborers could learn to work them. American capital and "know-how" were in great demand below the border. Everyone was talking about Mexico, but no one really knew much about it.

"It would make a good series," he admitted. "But I don't know about sending you, Nellie. Mexico follows Spanish customs. The Spanish would be horrified at a young woman traveling about by herself. Their girls can't even go to church without a chaperon."

"But I'd have a chaperon," Nellie said demurely. "I'd take my mother with me. There are reasons—well, I think she'd be happier out of Pittsburgh for a while. I'm not asking the *Dispatch* to pay our expenses," she explained. "With what you'll pay me for the articles, and Mama's little income, we can manage very nicely."

It took a little more argument, but finally she persuaded him.

She was in high spirits when she left the office. The trip itself would be fun. The first step in her plan to see the world and all its wonders. Her articles would be of real help to readers who might be thinking of going to Mexico. She was confident that she could make them interesting even to stay-at-homes. And last, but by no means least, she would get her beloved mama away from the boys and their nagging wives.

The travelers left for Mexico in the early autumn of 1886. They spent six months poking about the country, journeying by muleback to regions where the new railroads had not yet penetrated. Nellie's articles were so well received that Mr. Madden raised her pay. When she came back in the spring, she was earning fifteen dollars for a story.

This made her financially independent, with no need to ask Mama or the brothers for a penny. In other ways, too, her independence had grown. She was no longer a timid schoolgirl, but a successful writer. She had traveled in a foreign land. She was less inclined than ever to allow her brothers to dictate her life.

They tried. Now that she had had her fling, they urged, it was time to go back to a normal life. She could help Mama with the housework, do a little sewing and embroidery, and look around for a good husband. After all she was twenty years old now. The first thing she knew, she would be an old maid. And what could be a worse fate than that?

So far as Nellie was concerned, remaining unmarried held no terrors. She was far more interested in a career than in marriage. But even Mama held up her hands in horror at the thought of an old-maid daughter. She began asking anxiously if there weren't any nice young bachelors around the newspaper office. When she was a girl, Mama said reproachfully, she had had a dozen swains sighing at her feet. It did seem odd that her pretty, clever daughter had not even one!

Those days after her return were not happy ones for Nellie. Besides her family troubles, she found her job on the *Dispatch* unsatisfying. She had exhausted the working-girl problem in Pittsburgh. The city's chief industries, involving coal and steel, did not employ women. With no more factories to expose, she grew restless and anxious to change.

The idea came to her one sleepless night. Why should she stay in Pittsburgh? New York City had more newspapers, more factories, more slums. There must be endless material there for the sort of articles she liked best to write. Why shouldn't she try her luck with a New York paper?

Her first plan was to take Mama with her. But the

brothers would not hear of it. With Nellie so busy, what could their mother do with herself in a city boardinghouse? And the older lady's income would not be enough to purchase a home of her own in expensive New York. Much better, the brothers urged, for Mother to stay here. She could give up the house and live with each of them in turn, lending a hand with the children. After they had talked to her, they brought Mrs. Cochrane herself to agree that it was the better plan.

Nellie was too sensible to feel hurt. She would have no money of her own until she found a job. Once she did that and got firmly established, it would be a different story. Mama could live with her then. In some ways it was exhilarating to set out on her venture alone.

"If I go hungry at first," she told Mr. Madden, "it won't matter to anyone but me. I don't think I'll starve, though."

"I don't think you will," he agreed. "It may be a little tough to land a job. I wish I could help there. I'll give you some letters, but I don't carry much weight with the New York papers. The old *Dispatch* will miss you, girl."

"And I'll miss the *Dispatch*," she said sincerely.

She glanced around the shabby, dusty office. It had seemed such a frightening place when she made her first call. And now, with the clattering press and the smell of printer's ink, it was more homelike than her own home.

"I'll miss you too, Mr. Madden," she went on. "You —you've been awfully good to me. Next to my father, I think you're the *best* man I've ever known!"

A smile lighted his stern face.

"That isn't what you said in the first letter you wrote me, my young friend. 'Horrible old curmudgeon! Cowardly cad! Nasty and cheap and—oh, yes, abominable!' You used 'abominable' at least six times, as I remember. I hope at least I've taught you not to repeat your adjectives."

"You've taught me everything I know about the newspaper business," she answered. "And I don't mind your bringing up that silly letter now. It shows me how far I've come. 'Calling names proves nothing'—do you remember telling me that? It was my first lesson. And you've taught me so many, many more. I wish I knew how to thank you."

"No thanks needed," he said gruffly. "Licking cub reporters into shape is an editor's job. And I won't deny that I've done a good job with you. I'd like to keep you here, Nellie. But I think myself you're doing the wise thing. New York has opportunities far beyond anything Pittsburgh can offer. Let's see what you make of them."

Her eyes misted over as she took his outstretched hand.

"Whatever I do," she said gratefully, "I'll never forget where I got my start."

4   No Girls Wanted

Nellie's brothers did not object to the New York venture. If their young sister must go on with her newspaper career, it was better that she do it in a distant city.

Her mother's only worry was to make sure that she found a good home. It must be a place with regular meals, and someone to see that she wore her rubbers on rainy days.

A friend recommended a New York boardinghouse kept by a respectable widow. The landlady was said to be a kindly soul who looked after her guests like a mother, and who "set a good table" besides. It sounded exactly right for Nellie. She wrote and reserved a room.

Traveling alone for the first time in her life, she took the train to Jersey City, where the railroad ended. There she changed to a ferry boat to take her across the Hudson River to Manhattan Island.

The train had been hot and dusty, but she found the short ferry trip enchanting. The towers of Manhattan seemed to float above the blue water, their windows turned to blazing gold by the rays of the setting sun. Tall ships in the harbor fringed the shore, stretching up and down the river. Nellie's heart beat fast as the boat slid into the ferry slip, gateway to this magic city.

The motherly landlady had come to meet her. She led the way to the horse-drawn bus which took them to her house on upper Lexington Avenue.

It was a tall brownstone in a row of similar houses. The landlady explained that it had been the family home before her husband's death. Like so many widows of her day, she now supported herself by opening her home to paying guests.

Nellie was impressed by the handsome front parlor and the graceful stairway. The splendor faded quickly as she mounted the stairs. Her own room proved to be a tiny attic chamber, once a servant's room. It was simply furnished and stiflingly hot. But it was clean and cheap, and the landlady seemed kind. Nellie asked nothing more.

As soon as she was left alone, she drew out the list she and Mr. Madden had made. It contained the names and addresses of every newspaper in New York. Most of them were on Park Row, near the City Hall. "If the first one turns me down," she reflected, "I can try the next without spending more carfare. That's something, anyway."

Mr. Madden had warned her that she must expect to be turned down. "They just might give you a chance on the woman's page, writing about fashions and recipes. Oh, I know that isn't what you want, Nellie. You want to do real reporting. Well, not a paper in New York employs a woman to do the sort of thing you've been doing for us. If there's a place for you on a New York paper, you'll have to make it for yourself."

"I'll make it," she had told him confidently.

Her confidence was still high as she went over the list now. The *Sun*, the *Tribune*, the *Times*, the *Herald*, the *Post*, the *World*—oh, there were so many of them! All these editors couldn't be prejudiced against girl reporters. And even if they were, they couldn't be any more prejudiced than Mr. Madden had been at first.

He'd talked about having to make a place for herself here. Well, she'd had to do that on the *Dispatch,* too. And she'd done it. She could do it again. She *would* do it again.

She smoothed her hair and went down to supper. Her fellow guests, four or five middle-aged schoolteachers, were pleasant but distant. The conversation was all of school affairs, of which she knew nothing. As soon as the meal was over she escaped to her room. She unpacked quickly and was in bed by the time darkness fell. Tomorrow would be a long day.

It was shorter than she had expected. Following her landlady's directions, she took a horse car down to Park Row. By early afternoon she had visited every office on her list.

Not once did she get beyond the office boy. Some of them were civil, and some were curt. Each demanded to know what she wanted to see the editor about. When she admitted she was looking for a job, they told her flatly that the paper never hired women reporters.

As Mr. Madden had predicted, his letters of introdduction did no good. She was invited to leave them, with her address. The editors would write if they wanted to see her. No, it was no use asking them to see her now. That was what office boys were for; to keep their bosses from being pestered by unwelcome visitors.

She was more puzzled than discouraged as she left the last office. "Where did I go wrong?" she asked herself. She found a bench in City Hall Park and sat down to think it out.

"I can't say I've been refused a job," she told herself. "I haven't asked for one yet. Those boys couldn't hire me if they wanted to. It's the editor who does that. And I haven't seen a single editor. Now that's what I have to work out. How do I get into an editor's office?"

From where she sat, she could see the front doors of several newspaper offices. A trickle of men passed in and out. Any one of them might be the editor who could decide her whole future. What if she went up to him there on the steps? Grabbed his arm? Made him listen?

She shook her head. If she tried anything like that, the man could have her arrested for disturbing the peace. And very likely he wouldn't be an editor, anyhow. She mustn't waste her time in wild fancies. This problem called for some real thinking.

Sitting there in the shade, she thought long and hard. How had she got her job on the *Dispatch*? Not by going to the office and asking for it. She had attracted Mr. Madden's attention by writing him a letter. It was a silly letter. Just the same, it had brought her an invitation to visit the editor. And the visit had resulted in the job.

She sat up straight, her weariness forgotten. A letter to the editor—that was it. A very different sort of letter this time, though. Sensible and businesslike, telling of the work she had done in Pittsburgh. She had brought a scrapbook with her, containing all her published articles. She'd copy the best ones and enclose them in each letter.

Nellie was never without pencil and paper. She took out a pad now and began drafting her letter. All afternoon she sat on, deaf and blind to her surroundings. The homeward rush was beginning when at last she put the scribbled pad back into her handbag. Swaying from a strap in the crowded car, her mind went on forming words and phrases.

"I won't be wanting supper," she told her landlady on the way up to her room. For half the night she worked on, carefully copying the articles from her scrapbook. It was past midnight when she finished, too late to buy stamps for her half-dozen letters. She went to bed hungry and exhausted but supremely hopeful.

The letters went out next morning. She figured that she could not expect an answer for at least three days. Those three days she devoted to exploring New York.

There were wondrous sights to see. The Statue of Liberty, not yet one year old. The Brooklyn Bridge, one of the seven wonders of the modern world. The glittering department stores, the magnificent churches, the quaint foreignness of the immigrant neighborhoods. Nellie saw it all, by bus and streetcar, and on her own tireless little feet. She must hurry, she told herself, to learn her way around the city. It would help when she got her job.

She need not have hurried. The fourth day brought no job. Neither did the fourth week. A few editors wrote politely that they had no openings but would place her application on file. Most of them did not trouble to write at all.

Again Nellie had to ask herself, "Where did I go wrong?" Her letter and samples of her work were accomplishing nothing. This, then, was not the way to go about it. She must find another way.

She went back to her experience with Mr. Madden. She had first attracted his attention by criticizing an article in his paper. Suppose she tried that here?

She tried it. Every day she bought all the leading papers. She combed the editorial pages for an article to suit her purpose. When she found one, she sat down and wrote a reply. Sometimes she praised the article but added some reflections of her own. Sometimes she disagreed and gave her reasons for it. Neither plan worked. So far as any response was concerned, she might as well have dropped her letters into the East River.

The hot, steamy New York summer dragged on. Nellie had a spurt of hope when she read in the New York *World* of a proposed balloon ascension in St.

Louis. The *World's* owner, Mr. Joseph Pulitzer, also owned a St. Louis paper. He was sponsoring a bigger and better balloon, which would carry its passenger higher into the sky than man had ever gone.

Why should the passenger be a man? It occurred to Nellie that a girl passenger would be far more sensational. Men had gone up in balloons before. She could not remember that a woman ever had.

She dashed off a series of letters to Mr. Pulitzer, urging him to let her make the ascent. No answer came.

She began again to make the rounds of the newspaper offices. This time, instead of asking for a job, she came in with outlines of stories she would like to write. They were along the lines that had brought her success in Pittsburgh. The crowded firetrap tenements of the East Side, the lack of drinking fountains for work horses, the wretched plight of homeless children —there was no lack of material. If only she could make the editors see it!

Once in a great while she managed to talk her way past the office boy, to some harassed editorial assistant. "You can leave your outline," he would tell her grudgingly. "We'll let you know if we can use it." How she came to hate those well-worn words! They meant nothing but a polite dismissal.

Her worst day came toward the end of August. Up to now, she had had no money worries. The fund she brought with her was enough to pay her board, although it was melting fast. Carfares and newspapers were expenses she could not avoid. But there were still ten comforting ten-dollar bills in the little purse she carried in her skirt pocket. Money was safer there than in her beaded handbag, she thought. A bag might be snatched from her, but no one could even suspect the hidden pocket in the skirt's wide folds.

She took the horse car down to City Hall, and settled herself on her favorite bench in the little park. By this time, she knew all the editors by sight; when they arrived, and when they left their offices.

Today she was determined to make another attempt upon the *World*. The time for the balloon ascension was drawing near. If she were to persuade Mr. Pulitzer to let her be the passenger, she must do it quickly.

"I'll talk to him today or die in the attempt," she vowed, and settled down to wait. It would be an hour at least before the great man appeared at his office. She had watched often enough to know his usual time. It would be a tiring wait, but it was cooler here under the trees than in her airless little attic room.

"Lemonade, Miss?"

She looked up as a boy approached the bench. He was carrying an open pail of lemonade and a battered tin cup. Nellie did not usually buy from these street vendors. But the boy looked fairly clean, and ice tinkled invitingly in the pail.

"Ice-cold," he urged, seeing her hesitation. "I just brung it from home, Miss. Ain't nobody drunk out of the cup yet, if you're fussy."

"I'm pretty fussy," she admitted. Then she smiled down into the anxious young face. "All right. I guess it won't hurt me for once. You can pour me a cup, sonny."

She reached into the pocket for her purse. Her groping fingers failed to find it. She twisted on the bench, pulling the full skirt around. With both hands she held the pocket open. It was empty.

"I'm sorry," she told the boy. "I—I've lost my money."

With a scowl he poured the drink back into his pail and scurried off. She did not see him go.

"How could it have happened?" she was asking herself. "Did I leave it on my dresser? No, because I had it when I paid my carfare. Maybe I put it into my bag."

She turned out the little bag without hope. There was nothing there but her handkerchief and pencil and paper.

She thought back to her trip downtown. She had sat next to a fat woman with a bundle of washing on her lap. The woman had squirmed and shifted a good deal, but Nellie had supposed that was because the bundle was awkward. She must have seen Nellie pay her fare when the conductor came through. She would have seen her put the purse back into her pocket. Had the woman sat on the pocket side? Yes, she had. Those fat fingers constantly fiddling with the bundle must have crept into the hidden pocket.

That was how it happened. And now what? The hundred dollars was to have seen her through another two months. It was gone. She was left without even carfare to take her back to her boardinghouse. She would have to walk home. And borrow a stamp from her landlady to write to Mama.

Mama would send her some money, of course. But she was living with Albert this summer. It would not be possible to draw the money and send it without Albert's knowing. He couldn't stop Mama, of course. It was her money. But how he would gloat!

She wished now she hadn't written such cheerful letters. Things were a little slow in summer, she had said, but she had good prospects. Any day now she expected to have wonderful news of her new job.

"Well, this is the day," she told herself grimly. "I said I'd see Mr. Pulitzer today. Now I've *got* to see him. And he's *got* to give me a job!"

She could scarcely bear the waiting now. It seemed ages before her straining eyes caught sight of the Pulitzer horses. The carriage clattered across the cobblestones and drew up with a flourish before the *World* Building.

The coachman leaped down and opened the carriage door. Resplendent in frock coat and silk hat, his gold-headed cane gleaming in the sunlight, Joseph Pulitzer strolled leisurely up the low steps. A bowing doorman ushered him inside.

"I'll give him twenty minutes to get settled," Nellie decided. Her pretty face was pale, and her little fists were clenched with determination. "Then I'm going in there. And I'm not coming out until he's hired me."

5 The Great Mr. Pulitzer

But you can't sit here, Miss. You're in everybody's way!" The boy sounded a little desperate.

Nellie smiled up at him.

"I'll be glad to move into Mr. Pulitzer's office. But I'm going to sit right here until I see him. I told you that."

"Yes, and I told you you can't see him! I've told you and told you, Miss. *Nobody* sees Mr. Pulitzer, unless he sends for them. I don't dare go in there myself except when he rings for me. You'll just get me into trouble if you keep on sitting there."

"I'd hate to make trouble for you," Nellie said sweetly. "When I see Mr. Pulitzer, I'll tell him it wasn't your fault."

"But—oh, what's the use? Sit there, then. Keep on sitting till you get sick of it. But you'll never get near the boss."

He turned away in disgust. Nellie settled herself more firmly in her chair. At least she had penetrated to the *World's* city room, which she had never managed before.

It had been easy. She had just come upstairs and walked quietly through the open door as though she belonged there. No one but the office boy had paid her the slightest attention.

All about her was the bedlam of a newspaper going to press. Reporters were dashing in and out. Subeditors worked away at their desks. Once in awhile one of them got up to shout into a curious black box on the wall. Nellie had heard about a new invention called the telephone, but this was the first time she had seen one. The telegraph instrument clicking away in the corner was familiar from her *Dispatch* days. The *World* must be a very up-to-date paper, to have telegraph and telephone both.

If she had not been so worried, she could have enjoyed watching the city room sights. As it was, she could not get her mind off her troubles. If she left here without a job . . . ! But she wouldn't. She would sit right here until she got one.

The minutes dragged by, and still she sat, quietly waiting. On the far side of the room were two private office doors. One was closed. The other stood open, showing an untidy desk and empty chairs. She guessed that Mr. Pulitzer must be behind the closed door. Would it ever open for her? Oh, it must, it must!

"Excuse me, ma'am." A big man, coming in from outside, had nearly tripped over her feet. He caught the back of her chair to steady himself and looked at her in surprise. Then he frowned.

"Visitors are not allowed in the city room, young lady," he said curtly. "If you're a friend of one of the reporters, you'll have to wait for him downstairs."

The office boy hurried over to them.

"She's nobody's friend, Mr. Cockerill! She's just— well, she acts like a crazy woman to me. She's been sitting there all morning, and I can't make her budge. Will I call a cop and have him throw her out, sir?"

"Not yet." The big man turned to Nellie.

"I am John A. Cockerill, managing editor of this paper. If you have business here, tell me what it is. If not, I must ask you to go quietly before we call the police."

Nellie took a deep breath.

"I'm sorry to be a nuisance, Mr. Cockerill. But I came to see Mr. Pulitzer. I'm going to stay here until I do."

Her voice was soft but very firm. The editor looked puzzled. Then he gestured toward the empty office.

"Come in here," he said shortly.

Nellie hesitated. Then she got up and followed him. A quick glance showed her an inner door connecting with the other private office. Joseph Pulitzer, she knew, was behind that closed door.

Mr. Cockerill offered her a chair and sat down behind his desk.

"Now, young lady. You may take my word for it that you won't see Mr. Pulitzer unless I say so. I can give you five minutes to convince me. To begin with, who are you?"

"My name is Nellie Bly," she began eagerly. "And I want——"

"Nellie Bly? I've seen your letters. You're the young woman who wants to go up in the St. Louis balloon. Mr. Pulitzer has already made up his mind about that. The answer is no. And it's final. No amount of coaxing ever changes *his* mind. Now don't let's have any tears," he added hastily. "That's one reason women don't belong in business. They always burst out sobbing when things don't go to suit them."

There were tears in Nellie's eyes, but she blinked them back.

"I'm not going to cry, Mr. Cockerill. If you're sure Mr. Pulitzer won't change his mind—yes, I can see you *are* sure. All right. I won't bother him about the balloon. But I still want to talk to him. About something entirely different."

"You don't give up easily, do you?" There was unwilling admiration in his voice. "I know more about you than you might think, Miss Nellie Bly. You've written a number of letters to Mr. Pulitzer. They were all passed on to me. I take it you're in earnest about wanting a job on the *World*."

"Oh, I am, Mr. Cockerill!" Nellie's voice shook with eagerness. "Going up in the balloon was just one of my ideas. I have lots of others. New York is full of good stories that never get into the papers. All sorts of dreadful things are going on that need to be exposed. I'd like to do here what I did in Pittsburgh. Out there I—"

"Yes, you wrote us about your work on the *Dispatch*," he cut in.

Nellie flushed. It was plain that time was more precious here than in easygoing Pittsburgh. Cockerill saw her embarrassment and went on more kindly, "I'm a busy man, Miss Bly. So is Mr. Pulitzer. But I like your grit. I think you've earned your interview. I warn you, though, you must make it brief. Wait here."

He went to the inner door, knocked, and entered, closing the door behind him.

And now, for the first time, real panic swept over Nellie. The balloon plan was hopeless, she could see that. What else was there? What other idea could she offer that would get her a job?

She had told Mr. Cockerill that she had lots of them. But what did she have that was big enough, different enough, to offer Mr. Pulitzer? Her whirling brain could not produce one. If only she had time to think, to pick and choose!

But she had no time at all. In only a minute or two, the inner door opened. Mr. Cockerill beckoned to her.

The great Mr. Pulitzer sat behind his huge mahogany desk, frowning a little through his thick-lensed glasses. Although it was a well-kept secret at that time, his sight was failing fast. But except for his red-rimmed, bloodshot eyes, he was an extremely handsome man. He was tall and bearded, with an almost kinglike dignity. Hardier souls than Nellie's had quaked in that imperial presence.

He did not rise as Cockerill introduced her.

"Sit down, young woman," he ordered. "I hear you've taken a good deal of trouble to see me. Now let's hear what you want to see me about."

"Yes, sir." Nellie gulped. "I—I want to be a reporter on the *World*, Mr. Pulitzer. I've already had newspaper experience in Pittsburgh, and——"

He silenced her with an impatient gesture.

"We're not interested in your past. Cockerill says you claim to have some original story ideas. I doubt it. We have good men on the *World*, and they cover the city pretty thoroughly. But if you know something that hasn't been done, and that's any good, I'll listen. Make it brief."

Nellie's hands twisted desperately in her lap. Her mind was a complete blank. "She acts like a crazy woman to me," the office boy had said. If she didn't speak up now, Mr. Pulitzer would think the same thing.

Suddenly, out of nowhere, a great light came flooding in. She spoke without stopping to think.

"I want," she said deliberately, "to act like a crazy woman."

She paused, actually enjoying the amazement in the men's faces. This had been one of her most cherished story ideas. She had sent the *World* an outline of it weeks ago. They had paid no attention to it. Probably no one had even read it. She had almost forgotten it herself. But now it came back to her, complete in every detail.

"It would be sensational," she went on eagerly. "I'd get myself committed to the city asylum for the insane poor. I'd find out what really goes on behind those barred windows. Who knows how those poor people are treated? They can't complain, whatever is done to them. The authorities would just say, 'Oh, they're crazy, they're raving.' A lunatic is completely helpless. He has to eat what he's given, and do what he's told. The city spends a lot of money to keep up the asylum on Blackwell's Island. How do the taxpayers know what they're getting for their money? There are stories around town about waste and mismanagement over there. You must have heard them yourself, Mr. Pulitzer."

"Oh, stories," he said. "Of course I've heard stories. I once sent a reporter to the Island to look into them. But he didn't find anything amiss."

"Of course he didn't," she said scornfully. "Everything would be all tidied up for him. He'd see what he was meant to see and no more. But I wouldn't go as a reporter. I'd be a patient. I'd see it from the inside. And I'd stay long enough to find out just what conditions are. Then I'd write it up for the *World*. Don't you think your readers would be interested in such a story?"

She held her breath as the two men exchanged glances. Cockerill looked eager, but Mr. Pulitzer shook his head.

"It wouldn't do, Miss Bly. You are not insane. Patients are examined by a doctor before they are sent to the Island. You would never pass their examination. And even if you did—well, let me speak frankly. You seem to be a young lady of refinement. You could not endure life in the insane wards, if it is as bad as you think."

"For a good story, I can endure *anything*," Nellie said sturdily. "And I can fool the doctors. I know I can. I'll do it all on my own, Mr. Pulitzer. The *World* won't be connected with the scheme if it fails. All I'd want you to do would be to get me out after I'd had a week there. A week should be long enough."

"Getting you out mightn't be so easy, once you've been committed," Mr. Cockerill warned.

Nellie looked dismayed. But Mr. Pulitzer said easily, "There'd be no trouble about that. All it takes is for some respectable citizen to come forward and offer to give her private care. Our lawyer could do it. Once she was free and writing her stories, of course, it would all come out. I suspect there'd be some red faces around City Hall."

"Then you'll let me do it, Mr. Pulitzer?"

"You'd have to be honest," he said thoughtfully. "Things may be better over there than we think. The *World* doesn't deal in made-up horrors. We'd want whatever good things you find, as well as the bad."

"I understand that," she said eagerly. "I'll put down exactly what I see, Mr. Pulitzer, good or bad. All I care about is to find out the truth, and tell it. I always do."

Mr. Pulitzer glanced at his watch.

"Well, you've given us something to think about,

Miss Bly. I may say frankly that it's the most original idea we've come across in some time. We'll talk it over and let you know."

In bitter disappointment Nellie followed Cockerill back to his office.

"And I thought he was going to say yes," she mourned.

"He is." The editor laughed. "But he doesn't like to be hurried. Don't worry, Miss Bly. You're as good as on the *World* payroll right now."

A delighted smile chased away the gloom. After the dreaded presence of Pulitzer, this big, bearlike editor seemed an old friend. Impulsively she gave him her confidence.

"If I'm on the payroll, Mr. Cockerill, could I collect a little pay in advance? You see, I had my pocket picked, coming down here. I haven't a penny to get home."

"I'll give you a twenty-five-dollar order on the cashier—cash it as you go out," he said absently. "But don't go yet, Miss Bly. We'd better work out the details of this scheme of yours. When the big boss gives the word to go ahead, he'll expect action right away. Sit down here and tell me just exactly how you plan to turn yourself into a lunatic."

6   *Behind Asylum Bars*

One week later the matron of the charity Temporary Home for Females looked the new applicant over.

She saw a slender, nicely dressed girl with big, anxious eyes and tousled hair. The story she told was a simple one.

"My name is Nellie Brown. I have just come to the city. I have no place to stay. Will you take me in?"

"Have you any money?" the matron demanded.

Nellie pulled out a dainty purse and showed a half dollar and two dimes.

"But there is more, much more, in my trunks," she explained. "And all my jewels and the furs Papa gave me. I have to wait until my trunks come. May I wait here?"

"Well, I guess so," the matron answered doubtfully. "Although this is not really a place for young ladies. The Home is kept up for working women who are out of work and broke. We don't keep them more than three nights. You'd be better off at a hotel, Miss. Still—it's getting late in the afternoon, and I wouldn't know just where to send you."

Nellie shrank back. "Don't send me away!" she pleaded. "I won't be any trouble to you. Please let me stay!"

"Well, all right. I'll have to charge you thirty cents a night, since you can afford it. That's for bed and supper and breakfast."

Nellie nodded gratefully. "*Si, Señora,* I understand."

The woman stared. "A foreigner, are you? You don't look like one. Well, we get all kinds here. The girl will show you where you sleep."

Nellie followed the little maid of all work up the stairs. She was to share her room with three other women. They would be in by suppertime, the maid explained. That would be in about an hour. Nellie spent the hour sitting patiently on the fourth cot.

When the supper bell rang, she went down to the basement dining room. Some twenty women were gathered at the long table.

With rough good nature they tried to make the newcomer welcome. But Nellie answered only with "Yes, ma'am," and "No, thank you." She played at eating the wretched food for awhile and then suddenly pushed back her chair.

"You will excuse me?" she said. "I must go and wait for my trunks."

She settled herself in a chair by the window in the sitting room. There she stayed throughout the evening, answering no questions, looking steadily out of the window.

The other women spent the evening rocking and talking or playing cards. At nine o'clock the matron bustled in to tell them it was bedtime. By the rules of the house, all lights must be out at nine-thirty.

Nellie obediently followed her three roommates upstairs. But once in their room, she drew a chair to the window. "I must watch for my trunks," she told them.

The women laughed, but one of them spoke kindly.

"They won't be coming tonight, dearie. Get you to bed now, so we can put out the lamp."

Nellie turned her great eyes upon her. "I can't

go to bed until my trunks come, Señora. Because my silk nightgowns are in them. So you see I must wait."

A roar of laughter greeted her words. But the friendly one spoke coaxingly, "Now, now, you'll just strip off your dress and stays and petticoats and sleep in your underwear, the same like we do. None of us got nightgowns. We pawned all our spare clothes before we landed here. Come on, now, let me help you off with that dress."

"Don't touch me!" Nellie drew away. She looked wildly at the three women, now stripped down to their coarse muslin underwear.

"I must wait for my trunks," she insisted. "I can't go to bed without my silk nightgown."

So far she had spoken quietly and reasonably. Now all at once her voice rose.

"You must be crazy women!" she cried out. "Or else you'd have nightgowns. Everybody knows that lunatics tear up their clothes. That's it, you're crazy, every one of you! You've torn up your nightgowns. Now you haven't got any, and you don't want me to have any! That's why you hid my trunks. But they're here somewhere, and I'll find them. I'll find them——"

She jumped up and ran around the room, looking under beds, crying hysterically. Her roommates tried in vain to quiet her. In a few minutes the heavy footsteps of the matron approached the door.

"What is all this uproar?" she demanded.

Nellie flew to her and clasped her around the waist.

"Take me away from here," she begged. "I'm afraid of these crazy women! They've stolen my trunks, and now they're plotting to kill me. Oh, I won't stay here, I won't, I won't!"

She collapsed, sobbing, on the matron's shoulder. The woman looked over her head at the others.

"What have you been doing to her?" she asked sternly.

A chorus of indignant voices answered her. If anyone was crazy, it was the new girl. Thought she couldn't go to bed without her silk nightgown!

The grim-faced matron was not unkindly. She soothed Nellie as best she could, even taking her to her own room. But the girl refused all comfort. Sometimes she grew quieter, begging pitifully for her trunks. The next minute she would shriek that "those crazy women" were coming to kill her.

The poor matron spent an exhausting night. As soon as it was daylight, she called in the policeman on the beat.

The officer was a big, cheerful Irishman who seemed to win Nellie's trust at once. "You'll get my trunks back for me, won't you?" she asked him.

"That I will, Miss. You just come along with me. We'll go right down to the railroad office and see what's holding them up."

Nellie wiped away her tears and produced a smile.

Confidingly she slipped her hand in his. "You make me think of my papa," she said in a little-girl voice, and walked away at his side.

The "railroad office" was the police station, and later the Essex Market Police Court. Nellie told the same story to the desk sergeant and to the judge. She was Nellie Brown. She had lost her trunks. And she had spent the night in a house full of lunatics who tried to kill her.

The judge questioned her sharply.

"I forget, Señor," she said, wearily passing a hand across her forehead. "It has given me a bad headache, this terrible night in a crazy house. I remember nothing."

"You don't remember where you came from?" he persisted. "You use a Spanish word now and then. Are you a Cuban?"

Her eyes widened. "But of course, Señor. Havana. I live in Havana. How could I forget my beautiful home? And Papa, dear, dear Papa!"

"That's better," the judge grunted. "Just where in Havana is your home? And what is your father's name? Come now, my girl, speak up. I haven't got all day."

His harsh tone brought a new flood of tears. Even in her grief she looked very pretty. A reporter in the courtroom nudged his companion.

"The old grouch!" he whispered indignantly. "She's

loony all right, but he needn't treat her like a criminal. Let's stay and see the end of this. I think there's a story in it."

"I don't know. I can't remember!" Over and over Nellie repeated it, between bursts of sobs. The judge, his patience at an end, committed her to Bellevue Hospital for observation.

She spent three days at the hospital and was interviewed by three doctors. She answered their questions as she had answered the judge's. She didn't know. She couldn't remember. She only knew that she was surrounded by crazy people who wanted to kill her.

"You don't think I want to kill you, do you?" one doctor asked.

She laughed wildly. "You? Oh, no. *You* want to send me to Siberia! Well, you won't take me alive. I'd rather die than go there—all that ice and snow— and the terrible salt mines." She fell on her knees. "Oh, Señor, I beg of you, have mercy. Kill me if you will. But don't, don't send me to that terrible place!"

The doctor looked at his colleagues, who shook their heads. "We'll have to try again when she's calmer," one of them said. The matron was called to lead her away to the ward.

In the hospital room she was quiet enough. There was no use wasting her play-acting on fellow patients. For them she simply sat in silence, looking terrified and occasionally bursting into tears.

On her second day she was told that a reporter was asking to see her. This was the young man from a rival paper who had been in the courtroom.

The request dismayed her. She had succeeded so far in fooling doctors and nurses. Could she fool a sharp-witted newspaperman? For all she knew, she might have encountered him in her search for work. She refused to see him and put on such a display of terror that the head nurse sent him away.

The young man was as good a reporter as Nellie herself. He wrote his story anyway, drawing on what he had seen in the courtroom, and what he could find out from hospital attendants. By the time it was printed, Nellie had been adjudged insane and committed to the city lunatic asylum on Blackwell's Island.

The newspaper story made good reading. A beautiful young Cuban girl, alone in New York, who had suddenly gone mad. What tragedy caused her mind to snap? Where were the mysterious trunks, of which no trace could be found? What secret did they hold, hidden among the jewels and the furs?

The other New York papers took it up. One enterprising editor, translating "Brown" into Spanish, came up with "Moreno" as her real name. He set his Havana correspondent to running down all the Moreno families in the city. There were several of them, but none was missing a lovely young daughter.

Only the *New York World* ignored the case of the
demented beauty. Not a line about her appeared in
the *World*'s columns. Gleefully, Cockerill and Pulitzer
watched their competitors exhaust themselves in
fruitless speculation. By the time this was over, there
would be red faces in rival newspaper offices as well
as at City Hall.

Her employers did not get in touch with Nellie. She
had only their promise that her captivity would end
in a week. Actually, it was ten days before she was
finally called to the chief warden's office.

A well-known lawyer, Mr. Peter A. Hendrick, was
waiting there. He had already satisfied the authorities
that he represented the girl's friends, who would see
to it that she had proper care. She was released in his
custody.

Mr. Hendrick whisked her off to a hotel, where the
World had reserved a room for her. She sat up all
night writing the first installment of her story. She
titled it "Behind Asylum Bars." When it began appearing in the *Sunday World*, it rocked New York City
to its foundations.

The tale she unfolded was one of sheer horror. She
told of brutal attendants, of uneatable food, and of
inhuman punishments. Graphically she described the
"outdoor exercise" in the stone-paved yard, with
women roped together and driven like horses by a
vindictive nurse. She told of the Saturday night bath,

when forty-five women followed each other into the same tub of dirty cold water, and were ordered to stand in line to "drip-dry" afterward.

She wrote graphically of the eight-hour day spent on hard wooden benches, forbidden to talk or to move. This was in the "recreation room," which boasted a piano and some comfortable chairs to impress visitors. The nurses occupied the chairs. Nellie was punished when she tried to play the piano for her fellow prisoners.

All these things were bad. But even worse, to Nellie's indignant soul, were the stories she heard from the other patients. Some were as sane as herself. A German woman had had a fainting spell in the street. Because she could not speak English, she could not explain that she had missed the relatives who came to meet her ship. They had gone back to Boston, and she had wandered about the city for several days, looking for them. She was lightheaded with fever when the police picked her up. They could not understand her mutterings. She had been pronounced insane and sent to the Island.

Another inmate was a young household servant named Tillie Maynard. Tillie had had a long illness, which cost her her job. She had been taken in by friends, poor people who cared for her at some expense and trouble to themselves. She made a slow recovery and perhaps did not seem sufficiently grate-

ful. At any rate, they told her that she was being sent
to the country to get strong again. The next thing
she knew, the Asylum's doors had closed behind her.
She was well on the way to madness now, Nellie
wrote. But it was the horror of asylum life that had
toppled her poor harassed brain.

These stories, and many like them, flowed from
Nellie's pen in vivid detail. The *World*'s editorial page
took it up, bombarding City Hall with embarassing
questions. Did His Honor the Mayor know that such
things were going on? Were crooked politicians making a profit from human misery? Now that it had all
come out, thanks to the *World*'s fearless reporter,
what was the city going to do about it?

Mayor Abraham Hewitt had been elected the year
before on a good-government platform. He was an
honest, high-minded man, as appalled as anyone else
by Nellie's story. He personally led a group of city
officials and reporters on a tour of the Blackwell's
Island institution.

The tour had enough advance notice to allow the
"tidying up" Nellie had foreseen. Patients, warned of
dire punishment, dared not complain. The violent
ones, heavily drugged, were found peacefully asleep
in bed. The kitchens had had a hasty cleaning. The
visitors were urged to taste the evening meal. They
found it not unpalatable.

The German woman of whom Nellie wrote had

been released the day after the article came out. Tillie Mayard, whom the visitors saw, was unmistakably mad now, whatever she may have been when first admitted.

All in all, the inspection party did not find the picture as black as Nellie had painted it. It was still black enough to cause them to recommend a grand jury investigation. The result was an appropriation of three million dollars to modernize the institution and improve conditions for the inmates.

Blackwell's Island is Welfare Island now. It still holds a city hospital for the mentally ill, where qualified psychiatrists use every resource of modern science to bring disturbed minds back to health. Very little that is being done there now could have been done seventy years ago, when Nellie Bly was a "patient." Mental health is a subject on which practically nothing was known in her day. But the kindly, humane treatment of sufferers was possible in her time. It did not come about until she forced the decent citizens of New York to demand it.

It was the case of the Pittsburgh working girls over again. Nellie did not and could not cure all the evils she found. But she found them and dragged them out into the light of day, where public opinion could deal with them. For this, if for nothing else, Nellie Bly's countrymen owe her a great debt.

7 Watch Out for Nellie Bly

The success of her asylum story brought Nellie a permanent job with the *World*. She was taken on as roving reporter, free to seek out material and write it up in her own way.

She made the most of her opportunities. Two weeks after the last of the Blackwell's Island articles appeared, the *World* published another sensational Nellie Bly story.

This time her target was the crooked employment agencies which preyed upon immigrants. Posing as an ignorant Irish girl, Nellie paid excessive fees for jobs that did not exist. She was insulted and ridiculed and made the victim of a dozen petty rackets. One man sold her a "pass" to walk on the city sidewalks. She paid two dollars for a "life ticket" that was supposed to provide free rides on streetcars and ferries so long as she lived. There were other "passes" and "licenses" for varying sums. Nellie bought them all and used them to illustrate her story. Its publication brought a flood of letters from readers who had been victimized in the same way. Again, through its daring girl reporter, the *World* had scored over its competitors.

Nellie was just getting into her stride when important changes occurred at the *World*. Joseph Pulitzer's health was failing, and blindness was coming fast. He could no longer continue his active management of the newspaper. Heavy new responsibilities fell upon Mr. Cockerill's shoulders. He had no time to listen to Nellie's ideas and help her plan her campaigns. He turned her over to Morrill Goddard, of the *Sunday World*.

Mr. Goddard has been called "the father of the American Sunday paper." Under Pulitzer's direction he was building the *Sunday World* into the Sunday newspaper as we know it. Before Pulitzer's time there was little difference between a Sunday edition and a weekday one. The *World* was the first Sunday paper to be separated into sections: news, want ads, drama and music, and special features.

Nellie's stories came under the "special features" heading. From the first they were published in the *Sunday World*. Now she was to work directly with its editor.

Mr. Goddard proved as sympathetic as Cockerill had been. When Nellie had a story idea, she talked it over with him. If he disapproved it, she produced another. When he approved, he gave her a free hand to carry it out, backing her exposures by his own strong comments on the editorial page.

New York of the late 1880's was a fertile field for Nellie's investigations. She visited free clinics and charity soup kitchens and pauper lodginghouses. These agencies lived on contributions from kind-hearted New Yorkers. Some of them, maintained by churches and the Salvation Army, she found wholly praiseworthy. Others were mismanaged or scandalously corrupt, with most of the money going into the pockets of the operators.

Almost uniformly bad were the city institutions for the helpless poor. Attendants were political hangers-on who made no effort to earn their salaries. And as for the city's jails——!

Nellie learned about the women's prison in the

same practical way she had used with the asylum. She actually picked a pocket in a crowd, and was arrested and sentenced for it. Her "victim" was a fellow reporter, who had consented to press the charge against her. Nellie's vigorous article on jail life brought about the appointment of female guards to look after women prisoners. It also produced what was at least a temporary improvement in jail food.

These activities made new readers for the *World*, and new fame for Nellie. They made her some enemies in high places, too. The crooked officials she exposed could not have operated without political protection.

Nellie had no fear of politicians, high or low. To prove it she went up to Albany, the state capital. There she sought out one Ed Phelps, known as the "lobby king." Mr. Phelps, it was reported, could have any bill passed or killed at his pleasure. All he asked was to be paid for the job.

Nellie bribed him to kill a certain measure, and gleefully gave the story to the world. Her article began:

> "For I'm a Pirate King!
> I'm in the Lobby Ring!
> Oh, what an uproarious,
> Jolly, and glorious
> Biz for a Pirate King!"

She went on to name names and figures. Mr. Phelps's career was ended, and several assemblymen decided not to run for re-election. A prominent New York clergyman praised Nellie from the pulpit, calling her "an angel of light."

Her enemies had less flattering names for her. The trouble was, they could never spot her. She was a mistress of disguise. With wig and grease-paint she could turn herself into a trembling old lady or a homeless orphan boy.

As a troubled young mother, she invaded a notorious "baby farm." These places relieved parents of unwanted children, and no questions asked. The "matron" assured Nellie that for ten dollars her baby would be taken off her hands and placed for adoption.

Nellie paid the fee and promised to come back with the child. Instead, she wrote a scathing article called "What Becomes of Our Babies?" It brought about a police investigation that disclosed the horrifying facts. Children as young as five were shipped south to work in the cotton mills. Conditions in the "homes" were fearful, with beatings and starvation and neglect the rule. A high percentage of the tiny infants died mysteriously soon after admission.

Nowadays, orphanages and adoption agencies must be licensed and frequently inspected. This is one more reform that we owe to Nellie Bly.

It was the Sunday editor, Mr. Goddard, who called a temporary halt to her exposure stories.

"You've got them shaking in their shoes," he told her. " 'Watch out, it might be Nellie Bly,' is the word that's going around. Now I think you should try something on the lighter side. Your stories wring the readers' hearts. That's good, but we mustn't overdo it. We can't have them saying 'Nellie Bly? Oh, it's sure to be something sad or horrible. I'll just skip it.' Do you see my point?"

"No, I don't," Nellie answered indignantly. "The things I write about *are* sad or horrible. I don't make them up. They're going on right here in our city. And people ought to know about them."

"I don't say you shouldn't keep on telling them, Nellie. You've done splendid work so far. But I think it's time to pull up a little. We don't want the public to get the notion that you're just a common scold, forever finding fault. If they do, they'll quit paying attention to anything you say. And that's the last thing we want."

"It certainly is," she agreed. "I see what you mean, Mr. Goddard. Maybe you're right." She sighed. "Then I suppose you want me to give up the steam-laundry idea?"

"Not to give it up, my dear. Merely to postpone it. From all I hear, the laundry story isn't a pretty one. Let it wait a bit. Do a few cheerful stories first. The contrast will give more weight to your serious articles as they come along."

Nellie nodded. "I know you're right, Mr. Goddard. But I haven't come across any cheerful stories."

"That's because you haven't looked for them," he said briskly. Then his tone grew serious.

"Listen, my dear. We can't have you turning into one of those sour, narrow-minded reformers who can see no good in anything. You know the ones I mean. Well, they were like you once—young and earnest and eager to change the world overnight. It just isn't done that way. Our world has its faults, and we have to do what we can to remedy them. But no one person can remedy them all, nor all at once. No, not even you, my girl, whatever you may think. Your powerful pen isn't that powerful."

Nellie smiled ruefully. "You hit straight from the shoulder, don't you, Mr. Goddard? I suppose I deserve it. I guess—yes, I see now that I've been taking myself pretty seriously. It's stupid and conceited to think I can wipe out every evil I see."

"You can do your share," he reminded her. "You have, and you will. But our city isn't all evil, Nellie. There are good things in it, too. Pleasant things. Funny things. Go out and find some for me."

"Funny?" she echoed. "I've never tried to be funny in my writing, Mr. Goddard."

"Then it's time you began. Lighthearted laughter

is a blessed thing, Nellie. Don't despise it. Our readers have their own private sorrows and woes. If you can make them forget for a little, lose themselves in an amusing story, you've done something worthwhile. Don't you agree?"

"I never thought of it that way," she said slowly.

"Then think of it now." He rose in dismissal. "Find me a story with a chuckle in it. And don't come back until you do."

A story with a chuckle in it! All the way home she pondered that assignment. The editor's warning, for all its sharpness, was a helpful one. She shuddered at the thought of being known as—what was it he had said?—a sour, narrow-minded reformer. A common scold. If some humorous articles would save her from that, then humorous articles he should have.

She gave him a series of them in the next few weeks. The first one related her experiences at a matrimonial agency, where she had presented herself as a husband-seeker. The next described her attempt to learn ballet dancing. She spent a night in what was supposed to be a haunted house and saw nothing more ghostly than a mother cat with seven kittens.

Reading her lighter stories now, they do not seem very funny. Perhaps they were not terribly funny then. But they were gay and adventurous, and they pointed no moral. Thus they proved exactly what

Goddard wanted her to prove. Nellie Bly was no waspish faultfinder, but a normal girl with an open, friendly attitude toward life. This image in her readers' minds strengthened their trust when she went back to serious subjects.

Her growing fame brought financial ease to Nellie. She was not on a salary but was paid separately for each article. Requests to reprint them came in from out-of-town papers. The *World* had no objection, and Nellie began to make some extra money from the reprint sales.

Now that she could afford it, her thoughts turned to a home of her own. She had moved from her first boardinghouse to a better one, but the life was still not entirely to her liking. Sometimes she grew homesick for her mother's cherishing care and the feel of belonging to a family. Why shouldn't she have Mama come to live with her?

Mrs. Cochrane, when her daughter wrote to suggest it, was delighted. She was too loyal to complain, but moving from one son's house to another was not without its drawbacks. There was nothing she would like better than to settle down keeping house for Nellie.

The brothers, as usual, were not pleased. Their wives found Grandma very helpful with the children. But Mrs. Cochrane came to New York for a visit and did not return.

Nellie found a comfortable little flat, and Mama brought the familiar, well-loved furniture that both of them had missed. Nellie's twenty-first birthday had passed unnoticed a few months before. In August, 1888, mother and daughter held a belated celebration in their new home. Nellie declared, as she blew out her candles, that it was the happiest birthday of her whole life.

8 The Big Idea

Nellie always had difficulty finding material for her lighter articles. There were plenty of abuses to expose, but few story ideas that would interest and thrill without horrifying her readers. She was delighted, then, when she came across one in a book.

The book was Jules Verne's best-selling novel, *Around the World in Eighty Days*. Its hero, an Englishman named Phileas Fogg, had won a bet by circling the globe in that incredibly short time.

The story was an entertaining one, filled with adventures and narrow escapes. Nellie skimmed impatiently over these. Since she had taken up newspaper work, she had lost all interest in fiction. What did interest her about the book was its central problem. *Could* a man travel completely around the world in less than three months? It had never been done in real life. Why not try it and find out?

Greatly excited, she took her idea to Mr. Goddard, who was not impressed.

"Couldn't be done," he said briefly. "Now, now, don't tell me Phileas Fogg did it. He was a character in a book, and an author can make his characters do anything. It would never work for a real person."

"Now you're talking like Mr. Fogg's club friends," she accused him. "The men who bet him he couldn't do it. And he did do it!"

"He did it in a book. And granting that it could be done, it would have to be done by a *man*. Even Jules Verne knew that."

"Verne had it done by a man because it suited his story. A woman could have done it just as well. I could do it. I can do it. Think what it would mean to the *World*'s circulation, Mr. Goddard! Think——"

"Sorry, Nellie. I've more important things to think about. Now run along like a good girl and don't come bothering me with fantastic schemes."

"That's final?" she asked wistfully.

"That's final!" he barked. "Now get along with you."

Several months later she stormed into his office.

"You're going to do it, and you never told me!" she said breathlessly.

"Do what?"

"Sponsor a trip around the world, that's what! To see if it can be done in eighty days. It was my idea, Mr. Goddard, you know it was. I begged you to let me do it. You said it couldn't be done. And now——"

"I also said it couldn't be done by a girl," he reminded her. "Calm down, Nellie. Take a chair and let's talk sensibly."

He waited while she dragged a chair up to his desk.

"Now," he went on. "It's quite true that you were the first one to suggest such a trip. But you weren't the last. Lately we've been getting a lot of letters from readers. They've been reading Verne's book and arguing about it. They'd like us to settle the argument by sending someone to try it."

"I told you the readers would like it!" she broke in. "I told you that last year."

"I know, I know. I don't see the point of trying it when it's bound to fail. It can be done on paper, by figuring a perfect schedule. Ship to train, train to another ship, a carriage drive for the stretches where there are no railroads—oh, it sounds simple. But trains don't always run on time, even here in the United

States. They're worse in Europe. And ships are at the mercy of the weather. They can't guarantee exactly when they'll reach port. The traveler would have to gamble on making perfect connections every time. I still say it can't be done."

"But you're going to try it," she persisted.

"Yes, we are. Julius Chambers, the new managing editor, is all for it, and Mr. Cockerill left it to him. Chambers says it doesn't matter whether our man succeeds or fails. People will buy the paper every day to see how he's making out."

"Of course they will." Nellie considered for a minute. Then she asked bluntly, "Did you tell Mr. Chambers I want to go?"

He looked uncomfortable. "Well, no, Nellie, I didn't bring your name up. Mr. Chambers took it for granted that it would be one of the boys."

"And that's why you didn't tell me. The city room is buzzing with it, and I'm the last to hear. It was my idea in the first place, but you didn't even consider me."

"I'm sorry, Nellie. I wish you could see sense about this. A man might make it, although I don't think so. I know a woman couldn't. You must see the reasons against it."

"I don't, though." Her tone was dangerously quiet. "I'd like to hear them."

"All right, you shall. This trip would take you into

barbarous countries, among all sorts of people. Even a husky young man would need to carry a pistol to protect himself. The dangers would be far too great for a helpless female."

Nellie smiled. "My mother and I poked into some pretty wild regions of Mexico. We didn't carry pistols, and no one molested us. If that's your only objection——"

"It's not. There are dozens of others."

Nellie took a deep breath. It would not help to lose her temper. Mr. Goddard could often be persuaded but never driven.

She forced herself to say gently, "I'm sure there are other objections, Mr. Goddard. But I think I can meet them if you tell me what they are."

"Well, for one, there's your luggage. All those trunks full of frills and furbelows that you women can't live without."

"I can live without them. I promise you I'll carry less luggage than any man you can find. What else?"

"Oh—!" He gave a helpless gesture. "It's no use talking to me, Nellie. We've already decided to send a man."

She sprang to her feet, her good resolutions forgotten.

"Very well, then, send your man!" she said furiously. "Send him, and I'll start the very same day and beat him back to New York. Think that over, Mr. Goddard!"

She whirled about and left the office, her French heels clicking angrily down the hall. The editor looked after her in dismay.

He did not need to be told what was behind her threat. Any one of the *World's* newspaper rivals would be delighted to hire the sensational Nellie Bly. She had only to walk down Park Row to find a sponsor for her trip. Whether the trip succeeded or failed, the *World* would lose its daring girl reporter. And with her would go the readers who bought the paper for the sake of her articles.

With a sigh Mr. Goddard left his desk for the office of the managing editor. He found Julius Chambers in conference with George Turner, the business manager.

"Come in, Goddard, and give us a hand," Chambers said. "We're just laying out the route for this round-the-world venture. We think our man should——"

"You mean our girl," Goddard interrupted. "I have something to tell you, gentlemen. Our globe-circling traveler will have to be Miss Nellie Bly."

"Nellie?" The managing editor grinned. "By George, Goddard, that's an inspiration! Why didn't I think of it myself? Could we persuade her to go?"

"She's already persuaded herself," Goddard said dryly.

Rapidly he related his talk with Nellie and her final threat.

"If we don't send her, the *Sun* or the *Herald* will. She'll race our man and beat him, if I know Nellie. And even if she loses, she'll write stories that will lay his in the shade. Her heart is set on going. We can't stop her now, even if we give up the whole project."

"Well, who wants to stop her?" Chambers demanded. "This is the best thing she's thought up yet. A young, lovely girl, setting out alone to circle the earth. She *will* go alone, won't she? If she has to lug along a chaperon, and a guard, and a maid to look after her clothes——"

"She won't take any of those." Goddard sighed. "You fellows know I've never been in favor of this scheme. It was all very well for Jules Verne to have his hero dash around the world with the speed of light. But in real life it won't be so simple. I don't believe anyone, man or woman, could manage it in so short a time as eighty days. We'll just be made to look foolish if we try it."

"Yes, you've said all that before," Chambers reminded him. "The rest of us think it's possible. Cockerill and Mr. Pulitzer think so. The attempt is going to be made, that's certain. And to have it made by our girl reporter will be a stroke of genius. I only wish I'd thought of it myself."

"You'll be glad you didn't, when she runs into trouble," Goddard predicted gloomily. "As you just said, Nellie is young and pretty. What if she gets herself kidnaped in the Orient? It would be just like one of those sultans to take a notion to add her to his harem. Then what?"

"Then we'd get some grand stories," Chambers laughed. " 'My Life in the Harem, by Nellie Bly.' Don't mention such an idea to her or she'll fix it up on purpose. Seriously, though, I don't see any great risk. She's a bright, sensible girl, well used to taking care of herself. She's done it in some pretty tough places here in town, as we all know. I'm for sending her. What do you say, Turner?"

The business manager was a man of few words.

"It'll sell a lot of papers," he said briefly.

Chambers laughed. "That settles it. I'm afraid you're outvoted, Goddard."

"All right, I won't argue any more. There's just one thing, though. Will Mr. Pulitzer approve of sending Nellie instead of a man? Surely you'll have to ask him first."

"Yes, I will," Chambers admitted. "Cockerill will agree, I know. He thinks there's no one like Nellie. But he's out of town. Anyway, Mr. Pulitzer might see the same objections to sending her that you do, Goddard. We couldn't go ahead without consulting him. I'll write to him tonight. Don't say anything to her until we hear. It would be cruel to disappoint her."

"*She* won't be disappointed," Goddard declared. "She's going around the world, for us or for some other paper."

"Well, it's got to be for us," Chambers answered. "I'll make that letter a cablegram. And I'll telegraph Cockerill in St. Louis to send one too. He has more influence with the big boss than I have. We ought to hear in a day or two."

Joseph Pulitzer, the *World's* owner, was then in Europe. American doctors had failed to help his dimming eyesight. He was traveling from one European city to another, consulting the leading foreign specialists.

The cablegrams reached him in Paris. His secretary did not think the matter important enough to bring it to his attention. Nearly three weeks went by before his answer finally came.

They were anxious weeks in the *World* office. Nellie had to be told just how matters stood. The delay, for which no one knew the reason, seemed to be against her. Mr. Pulitzer had already agreed that a man reporter should make the trip. It would be like him to indicate by this silence that he had not changed his mind.

Poor Mr. Chambers had to decide on a man in

case Nellie's plea was rejected. He chose Johnny Jennings, a brilliant young reporter recently added to the staff. When two weeks had gone by with no word from Paris, Jennings was called into the office of George Turner, the business manager.

"Looks like you're elected," Turner told him. "Here is the latest schedule, worked out for the coming week. They get out of date pretty quick. But if we got the word right now, you could catch the *Augusta Victoria* on the fourteenth. That would get you to London in time to cross the Channel and go by train to Brindisi, Italy. A P.&O. steamer leaves Brindisi on November 25. Then——"

He went over the route step by step. It all hinged upon the timetables. Oriental sailings were few and far between. A missed ship anywhere along the line could mean a delay of several days. And an eighty-day schedule must allow for very little wasted time.

Young Mr. Jennings went home in high spirits and packed his bags. He thought, as everyone was beginning to think, that the prize was his.

What Nellie Bly thought, she kept to herself. Mr. Turner had no chance to show her the schedule, for she did not appear at the office. She had agreed to make no move until Mr. Pulitzer's decision came. Instead of coming in for her weekly story conference, she wrote Mr. Goddard that she was busy planning a new series, of which he would hear later. He shuddered and wondered if he would hear of them through the columns of a rival newspaper.

The long-delayed answer came in the late afternoon of November 12. Joseph Pulitzer had the highest regard for Miss Nellie Bly as a resourceful young reporter. He thought her an excellent choice for the round-the-world venture. Please give her his best wishes for a happy and successful journey.

Chambers sent his own carriage to bring Nellie to the office without delay. She was smiling and self-possessed as she entered and took his outstretched hand.

"Congratulations, my warmest congratulations!" he boomed. "I'm as happy about this as you are, Nellie."

"I think you're more surprised than I am," she told him. "I never doubted that Mr. Pulitzer would see reason. Now tell me. When do I start?"

He picked up the schedule from his desk. "That's the trouble. You'll have to wait a week for your ship to England. The one we have listed here, the *Augusta Victoria*, sails day after tomorrow. You'd never get ready in that time, so——"

"I could get ready if it sailed tonight," she told him serenely. "Of course I'll take the *Augusta Victoria*, Mr. Chambers. Now let's see the rest of the schedule."

Her cheeks were pink with excitement when she arrived home, a little late for supper.

"I'm going to start around the world day after tomorrow," she told her mother in an offhand manner.

The older woman looked at her shrewdly.

"You're not fooling me, honey, pretending to be so calm. The way you've been worrying, moping around the house, and not even reading the papers! You've been just sick for fear they wouldn't let you go. And now they've said you can, don't tell me you don't feel like dancing!"

Nellie laughed. "And if I do, can you blame me? Oh, I talked big about how I'd make the trip for another paper, but it was just bluff. How did I know they'd let me, if Mr. Pulitzer wouldn't? But all my worry was for nothing. I'm going! I'm going day after tomorrow!"

"Well, if you are, you'd better start getting ready. We'll have to sit up all night, sorting out your clothes. I suppose you've already planned what you're going to take?"

"I hadn't the heart," Nellie admitted. "It seemed so hopeless, I just didn't want to think about it. But don't worry, Mama. I'll go out and buy my traveling wardrobe tomorrow. Tonight I'm taking you to the theater, as I promised."

9   Around the World

Early next morning, Nellie sought out Mr. Ghormley, a well-known ladies' tailor.

"I want one good dress that will stand three months' constant wear," she told him. "And I want it finished and delivered tonight. Now don't waste time telling me it's impossible. If you can't do it, I must find another tailor who can."

Ghormley's pride was touched. "If it can be done,

it can be done in my establishment, Miss Bly. May I ask the reason for this extraordinary haste?"

"Certainly." She smiled at him. "I'm starting around the world tomorrow. I shall wear your dress for the entire trip. Now may I see some materials, please?"

After some discussion they decided on a blue broadcloth, to be trimmed with plaid camel's-hair cloth. It was a two-piece garment, so that she could wear the skirt with a thinner blouse in warm climates.

She left the tailor's for a department store, where she bought a checked wool coat with matching cap, and an alligator traveling bag. The bag was about the size and shape of the ones that airlines nowadays furnish to their passengers. It was the only piece of luggage Nellie carried on her trip.

She hurried home to find that Mama and a neighbor had done the minor shopping she had requested. The two ladies had laid in a generous supply of veils, toilet articles, pins and needles, thread, handkerchiefs and collar ruchings. With her slippers and several changes of flannel underwear, these just about filled the bag.

The neighbor, Mrs. Cora Linn Daniels, had pressed Nellie's best silk dress and laid it out on the bed.

"I declare, I don't believe you can squash it in there," she said regretfully.

"Then I'll leave it behind. My water flask and drinking cup have to go, and plenty of paper and pencils. We'll leave out the spare gloves too. I'll just wear my black ones all the time."

She glanced at her watch. "I must get back to the office—they'll have my expense money and passport ready. Then I have to go to Ghormley's for my fitting. Don't wait supper for me."

She kissed her mother hastily. At the door she beckoned to the neighbor.

"Walk to the car stop with me, will you?"

As soon as they were outside she said earnestly, "Mrs. Daniels, I want to ask a big favor of you. I can't go off like this and leave Mama all alone in the flat. She's not too strong. She'll be lonely, and she's bound to worry about me. Could you come and stay with her until I get back? I'd be so grateful."

"Well, I don't know why not," Mrs. Daniels answered. "I'm a lone widow without chick or child. The cousin I'm living with is pretty crowded since her last baby came. Your mother's my best friend, Nellie. If you think she'd like it, I'll be glad to move in."

Nellie gave her hand an impulsive squeeze. "She'll be tickled to death, and so will I. Now I can start off with a light heart."

The start was made the following morning.

Compared with the tumultuous scenes of her return, it was a quiet affair. Her mother and Mrs. Daniels, Julius Chambers, and a few men from the *World* staff saw her off at Hoboken.

There was also a timekeeper from the New York Athletic Club. It was this gentleman's business to note from his stop watch the exact second at which the trip began. He would also be on hand to clock the finish.

The North German Lloyd steamer *Augusta Victoria* left Hoboken pier at 9:40 A.M. on November 14, 1889. Her fellow passengers saw a pretty girl in a checked coat waving to the small group on the dock. She carried a raincoat over her arm, a small alligator bag, and a copy of the morning *World*.

The passengers, arising early to catch their ship, had not had time to read the paper. They might have passed over the modest announcement in any case.

The big, screaming headlines came next day. Julius Chambers, with his rivals in mind, had kept the project dark until Nellie was well away. Fair play made him give out the news before she actually left, but he made it an inconspicuous item likely to be overlooked. This round-the-world trip was a *World* idea entirely, and he meant to keep it that way.

A curious little episode later in the day proved that the editor's caution was well founded.

Mr. James Brisben Walker was editor of *The Cosmopolitan*, a monthly magazine. Reading the November 14 *World* at breakfast, he found the brief statement of Nellie's venture. Mr. Walker was a man who prided himself on quick decisions. He had an inspiration and acted on it with lightning speed.

That evening Chambers' office boy announced Mr. Walker of *The Cosmopolitan.*

The magazine editor was beaming. He had added something new to the globe-circling idea, something sensational.

"A race, Mr. Chambers—a race between two beautiful young ladies, traveling in opposite directions. One goes east, one goes west. They cover the same route. Which will reach home first? The eyes of the world will be upon them. The most unique race in history. What do you say to that?"

Chambers was too dumfounded to say anything. He listened silently while Walker explained how the idea had come to him out of the blue. He had immediately sought out one of his writers, Miss Elizabeth Bisland, and commissioned her to start around the world that very day. He had just seen her off on a train bound for San Francisco.

"What do you think of that?" he repeated.

"I think nothing of it," Chambers answered icily. "Your purpose is clear, Mr. Walker; free publicity for your magazine. I may say that if *The Cosmopolitan* desires mention in the *World*, our advertising columns are open to it at the usual rates. Miss Bisland's journey has no value for us. I bid you good day, sir."

Pride would not let Walker recall his representative since she had actually started. Elizabeth Bisland made the trip and duly reported it in the pages of *The Cosmopolitan.* By the time her story appeared, Nellie Bly was firmly established as the world's most famous woman traveler.

She reached England six days after sailing and crossed at once to France. There she found time to pay a hurried visit to Jules Verne. He was surprised but pleased to find that anyone would take his book so seriously.

Nellie went on by train from France to Brindisi, Italy, where she boarded a P. & O. steamer. The *Victoria* took her through the Suez Canal and the Red Sea, out into the Indian Ocean with a stop at Ceylon, then to Singapore, and to Hong Kong in time for Christmas. There were days ashore at various ports along the way, while the ship unloaded cargo. She had a four-day wait at Hong Kong before her ship went on to Yokohama in Japan.

If this brief sketch of the world-shaking trip sounds tame, the sad truth is that the trip itself was a pretty tame affair. When there was time in port, Nellie went sight-seeing. So did her fellow passengers from the ship. The *Victoria* was British, serving British settlements in the Orient. Her passengers, Nellie included, saw and did nothing that differed from the standard tourist attractions.

No one on the *Victoria* saw anything extraordinary about Nellie's journey. They had heard that Americans were always in a hurry. Nellie's project of circling the globe in record time seemed to prove it. All very well if one wanted to do it, but why make a fuss about it?

The fact that she was a girl traveling alone failed to impress them. There were several English girls aboard, going out to join their families in the colonies. One was a schoolgirl of fourteen. A young woman who behaved discreetly was safe on a British ship and safe ashore wherever the British flag waved. Why should Americans imagine that danger lurked in the Orient?

This attitude does not mean that Nellie was unpopular. Far from it. She was pretty and gay, pleasant to everyone, eager to join in whatever amusement was going. She danced with the young officers, wound knitting wool for old ladies, entered with zest into every sight-seeing excursion. So far as her fellow passengers were concerned, she was simply a nice well-bred American girl enjoying a vacation cruise.

All the excitement of her trip was back in New York. Most of it was in the *World* office. Nellie was an honest reporter. She could not invent dangers and escapes where none existed. The accounts she sent in from every stop were disappointing in their lack of dramatic action. Her employers had to settle on the time element for reader interest. Would she, could she, make it in eighty days or less? That was the big question.

According to the *World*, that question was on everybody's lips. Actually, there were plenty of people in New York City who did not even know that Nellie had left home.

These were the misguided readers who bought the *Sun* or the *Tribune* or the *Times*. The *World's* competitors ignored Nellie completely. Their readers could follow the revolution in Brazil, and speculate on the future of the deposed emperor. They could read the latest wrangle over whether New York or Chicago was to be the site of a mammoth World's Fair. Or they could cluck their tongues over the respected post office cashier who made away with twenty-five thousand dollars of Uncle Sam's stamp money before he shot himself.

The rival New York papers found plenty of news to print without mentioning Nellie Bly. The out-of-town papers were more generous. They could afford to be, since they would not lose readers by it. But in New York City Nellie's well-wishers had to follow her progress in her own paper or not at all.

The *World* had a hard time keeping interest alive until Nellie reached Yokohama in Japan. There she boarded a new ship, the *Oceanic*, for the voyage across the Pacific to her homeland. Once landed in

San Francisco, she would have only an overland train journey between herself and her goal. The real race against time would begin with these last two laps.

The *Oceanic* left Yokohama on January 7 of the new year, 1890. Nellie had already used up fifty-five days of the eighty allowed her. With fair weather, the *Oceanic* counted on about two weeks for the Pacific crossing. But the weather reports were bad. Midwinter storms were raging in the Pacific, with harrowing reports of vessels lost at sea. Others, badly damaged, limped into port weeks after their predicted date.

"Will This Be Nellie's Fate?" the *World* asked in a headline. The headline covered an interview with a handful of survivors who had drifted for days in an open lifeboat. Nellie's loyal public shuddered and bought the *World* every day to make sure that if disaster overtook her they would know about it.

Ships of those days had no radios, and the *Oceanic* planned no stops after leaving Japan. The only news could come from other ships passing her at sea. As it happened, no other vessel reported sighting her on this voyage. Now the suspense which the *World* was trying to build up grew very real.

Nellie's editors made the most of it. Declaring that "our Nell" would reach port if she had to swim, they set their readers to guessing the date of her arrival in New York. Every day a Nellie Bly Contest blank appeared in the paper. The reader had only to fill in the exact day, hour, and minute when Nellie would step off the train at Jersey City. The prize for the most nearly correct answer was a trip to Europe, all expenses paid, and two hundred and fifty dollars in cash for spending money.

Coupons flooded the newspaper office. Not all of them came from *World* readers. Newspapers in San Francisco, Chicago, Cincinnati, St. Louis, and Boston were following her trip in their columns. So were many small-town papers. The *World* graciously allowed them all to reprint the coupon and invite their readers to join the contest. Nearly a million guesses were made. The winner was a Mr. F. W. Stevens, of New York, who came within two seconds of the official time.

Besides the guessing contest, the *World* put out a Nellie Bly parlor game. This was so successful that a toy manufacturer bought the right to make it for sale. The game was a bright-colored board marked into squares, complete with counters and a spinner. Players spun for moves upon the board, with the winner the one who first reached a center square lettered "Jersey City."

Many old-timers will recall playing "Around the World with Nellie Bly." It became a standard parlor game, continuing popular long after Nellie herself was forgotten. A few sets may still be found in old attics, too well loved to throw away.

The winner of the game had only to make a lucky spin to reach Jersey City and home. Nellie had the storm-tossed Pacific Ocean to cross.

As on the rest of her journey, the dangers here proved more imagined than real. The stout little *Oceanic* ran into rough weather and rode through it without mishap. She reached port safely on January 21, just two weeks after leaving Japan.

10 Seeing Nellie Home

Nellie stepped ashore to a tumultuous welcome. The San Francisco *Examiner* had alerted its readers for her arrival. Although it was only eight o'clock in the morning, a cheering crowd was on hand, waving flags and pelting her with flowers.

She was photographed on the dock and then rushed immediately to her waiting train. There a distinguished group had assembled for a ceremonial breakfast. They were city officials, reporters, and railway men, with their wives and daughters.

Speeches were made and toasts were drunk. Nellie heard enough compliments to turn her pretty head. For the first time since leaving home, she was made to feel that her exploit was important. The stodgy British may have thought little of it. But to her own countrymen she had done something wonderful. Something, as one speaker put it, "to show envious Europe how Father Time himself is outdone by that rare flower which flourishes only in the free air of Liberty—The American Girl!"

When Nellie had acknowledged the speeches with becoming modesty, she inquired about arrangements for the last part of her journey. The breakfast was being held aboard the private railway car of the road's president. Now she learned that this was to be her car as far as Chicago.

Mr. R. A. Donaldson, general passenger agent of the Southern Pacific, explained the situation. There had been heavy snowfalls in the Sierra Nevada Mountains, blocking rail traffic. Snowplows were working frantically but it might be some time before the service was restored.

It had been decided, therefore, to send Nellie by a special route through the Southwest. Competing railroads had generously offered the use of their tracks. The Southern Pacific had made up the special train,

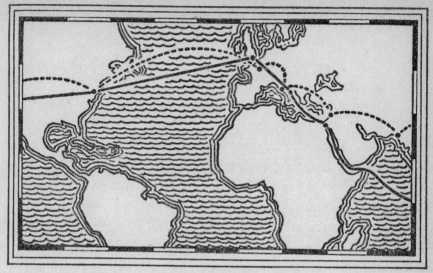

Nellie Bly's Trip in 1889-90

consisting of the engine and the private car. The Central Pacific would give it right of way, and it would use Atchison, Topeka & Santa Fe tracks into Chicago. Only the most urgently necessary stops would be made.

Nellie listened with interest.

"No trains have been coming through? Then that accounts for something that has been puzzling me. I thought surely someone from the *World* would come to meet me."

Mr. Donaldson explained that an escort corps from the *World* was aboard a train snowbound at Emigrant Gap. The train had been stalled there for four days.

"There's a telegraph station at the Gap," he went on. "We've had some frantic messages from a Mr.

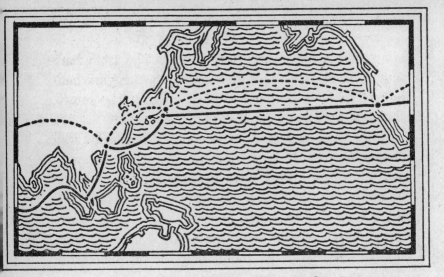

--------- *Route of Present-Day Airplane Trip*

Jennings of the *World*. But of course there's nothing we can do until the snowplows break the way."

Nellie's special began its run at 9:00 A.M., less than two hours after her ship docked. Mr. Donaldson and an *Examiner* reporter named Charles Law accompanied her. They were two hours out when the train halted on signal at a wayside station called Lathrop, California.

The reason for the halt was a dramatic one. The *World*'s reporter, Johnny Jennings, had made an eight-hour hike on snowshoes to the railroad track. He had never been on snowshoes before, and his guide was an old prospector who collapsed in sight of the goal. Jennings himself was near exhaustion.

The two half-frozen men were hauled aboard and revived with warm blankets and hot drinks. Jennings had a harrowing story to tell. The train had run short of food and fuel, several passengers had fallen ill, and suffering had been intense. The snow-shoe trek itself had been fearful.

Nellie had expected to encounter hardship and danger abroad. It is strange but true that the only real adventure arising from her trip came to Johnny Jennings, who had been passed over in her favor. If he felt any resentment, he must have been comforted by the warm reception of his Emigrant Gap stories. They laid the foundation for his successful career as a star reporter.

The special train sped across desert and mountain, pausing only to take on coal and water. For one level stretch the engineer let Nellie ride in the cab and take the throttle. Lonely cowboys stared as the special whizzed by, with a pretty girl waving them a gay greeting from the engineer's window.

At Albuquerque there was time for a delegation to come aboard, and a hasty newspaper interview. A brass band outside played "Nellie Bly," and "My Nellie's Blue Eyes," and "Nellie Was a Lady." They had also rehearsed "Seeing Nellie Home," but the train pulled out before the leader could raise his baton.

At La Junta, Colorado, the band had settled on "Seeing Nellie Home" as the most appropriate choice. They played it through six times while she waved and smiled and blew kisses from the rear platform.

Even the briefest halt was long enough for gifts to be offered and accepted. The car filled up with fruit and California wine, nuts and homemade cakes, Indian pottery and blankets, potted cacti and silver jewelry. Mayors presented the "keys to the city" of towns whose names she had no time to learn. And everywhere the flags waved and the bands tootled and the crowds shouted themselves hoarse for dauntless Nellie Bly.

Nellie was astounded at the warmth of her reception.

"These people out here don't read the *World*," she remarked to Johnny. "How did they know about me?"

"You underestimate the power of the press, Nellie," he answered. "These small-town papers get their city news from the big city dailies. They've been feeding Nellie Bly to their readers for years. And this trip is the perfect human-interest story. No politics in it, nothing distressing, and nothing that's hard to understand. Just a pretty American girl doing what every American girl would like to do. And showing the foreigners an American girl can do it, all by herself. Of course they're pleased—and proud of you. Here, we're pulling up for water. Out on the platform now, and give them that smile of yours."

It was not hard for Nellie to smile. She loved every

minute of it. At Chicago, where she left her special for a regular train, there was a two-hour wait. This was long enough for a group from the Chicago Press Club to escort her to their clubroom for breakfast and some flattering speeches. The club was an all-male one, and Nellie's was the first feminine foot to cross the sacred threshold. In the opinion of the Chicago Press Club this was the highest honor she received anywhere.

Her final change of trains was made at Philadelphia. The Pennsylvania Railroad had organized a mammoth reception there. One of their crack passenger trains was to be named for her. The "Nellie Bly" ran for many years between New York and Atlantic City.

Julius Chambers and several others of the *World* staff came from New York for the Philadelphia reception, bringing Nellie's mother and Mrs. Daniels with them. There were newspaper men from Pittsburgh, her home town, and Cincinnati and Boston.

All these friends, and many more, boarded the train at Philadelphia for the final run into Jersey City. An elaborate luncheon was served aboard. Nellie ate with one hand, the other tightly clasped in Mama's. The little old lady was awed to silence by the impressive company. But she beamed with pride when her Nellie stood up and answered the speeches with perfect self-possession. Nellie had had a good deal of practice at it by this time.

Jersey City was in *World* territory, and at Jersey City Nellie saw all the other civic welcomes surpassed. The dingy railway station had been turned into a bower of evergreens. A red carpet ran the length of the platform, with a group of little girls ready to strew it with crepe-paper roses.

There was a flag-draped speaker's stand, and so many bands that the one from the Newsboys' Home had to stand outside in the cold January wind. The newsboys were rewarded by being first to see the approaching train and first to strike up "Yankee Doodle." One of the other bands favored "Hail Columbia," and still another, a brand-new number, "Nellie Bly on the Fly."

So a fine burst of discordant music greeted Nellie's ears as the train thundered in and pulled to a dramatic stop, with bell ringing and whistle blaring. Three official timekeepers occupied the speaker's stand, eyes glued to their stop watches.

There was a brief delay, and then Nellie stood poised on the steps, waving her cap. She jumped lightly to the platform. The watches registered the exact time. It was 3:51 P.M., Saturday afternoon. The date was January 25, 1890.

The timekeepers consulted together, did a bit of figuring, and announced the time for the complete journey. From the second that the *Augusta Victoria* pulled away from the Hoboken pier, exactly seventy-two days, six hours, eleven minutes, and fourteen seconds had elapsed. Nellie Bly had beaten Jules Verne's imaginary record by nearly eight days.

Nellie chose the shortest route and the fastest transport available at that date. If she were doing it today, of course she would go by air. Here is the way the two trips would compare:

Then—1889-90			*Now—(by jet plane)*		
Nov. 14	Leave	New York	Nov. 14	Leave	New York
" 22	"	London	" 14	"	Paris
" 25	"	Brindisi, Italy	" 15	"	Rome
" 28	"	Suez, Egypt	" 15	"	Beirut, Lebanon
Dec. 18	"	Singapore, Malaya	" 16	"	Karachi, Pakistan
			" 16	"	Hong Kong, China
" 28	"	Hong Kong, China	" 16	"	Tokyo, Japan
			" 16	"	San Francisco
Jan. 7	"	Yokohama, Japan	" 17	Arrive	New York
" 21	"	San Francisco			
" 25	Arrive	New York			

(Both schedules allow for extra day gained at international date line)

Time: 72 days, approx. 7 hours.   *Time:* 3 days.
Cost: $805.00   *Cost:* $1,263.25

11 Gold and Glory

Any American girl could have done what I did," Nellie modestly told her cheering public.

This was certainly true. Its truth was proved four days later, when Elizabeth Bisland of *The Cosmopolitan* came quietly home. She too was an American girl who had undertaken to circle the globe in less than eighty days. There were no bands and speeches and cheering crowds for her. No one was on hand to check her time, which added up to seventy-six days. She had lost to Nellie by four days, but she was still four days ahead of the Verne schedule.

Elizabeth made the best of her defeat, turning out a series of straight travel articles. She had a keen eye for native sights and customs, and her description of life in the Orient pleased *Cosmopolitan*'s readers. She went on to literary success as biographer of Lafcadio Hearn, a popular author of that day. But the round-the-world feat brought her nothing but heartache.

It brought Nellie Bly everything that any heart could hope for. She had done only what anyone could do, but she had done it first. By that lucky chance she reaped all the extraordinary rewards that come for a first performance.

The rewards were tremendous. The first hint came after she had left the ferry from New Jersey and stepped into her carriage on the Manhattan side. Down Broadway she rode, at the head of a parade, with crowds lining the sidewalks, with cannons booming and fireworks lighting the winter sky.

The carriage halted for a minute while mounted policemen cleared the way. A silk-hatted man stepped forward and tossed a bunch of violets in Nellie's lap. A note was attached to it. She read the note hastily as the parade moved on. The manager of the Union

Square Theatre invited her to name her fee for a Sunday night lecture on her experiences.

The enterprising gentleman from Union Square was only the first to bid for personal appearances. In the next few days the *World* office was flooded with letters and callers. Audiences everywhere were demanding to see the glamorous Nellie Bly, and to hear her story from her own lips. Magazines offered fantastic sums for articles. She was urged to endorse face powders, corsets, luggage, and a self-wringing mop. All these products were to be rechristened the "Nellie Bly." Their makers offered to pay generously for the privilege.

The *World*, of course, was expecting her to come back to her old job. But Mr. Chambers, whom she consulted on the new offers, gave her some shrewd advice.

"Better cash in while you can," he told her bluntly. "You're a fad, Nellie. Oh, the biggest one that's come along since Jenny Lind, I'll admit that. But a fad, just the same. The public will get enough of you in time. You can always go back to newspaper work. But right now, if I were you, I'd rake it in with both hands."

Nellie took his advice. She signed with Mr. Hill, of the Union Square Theatre, for a series of forty lectures. Three were given in New York and the others out of town. She tried all the products the manufacturers sent her. If she found them satisfactory, she granted the use of her name. Her account of her trip, after publication in the *World*, was expanded into a book that sold thousands of copies. The Nellie Bly game was selling faster than the manufacturer could turn it out.

Nation-wide fame was hers, and more money than she knew what to do with. Her brother Albert came on from Pittsburgh to make some helpful suggestions about the proper use of all that money. Albert had quite forgiven his sister for disgracing the family name. He was even willing to move to New York and devote his talents to managing her fortune.

For Mama's sake, Nellie was cordial to him. She gave him some small sums to invest for her. But she made it very plain that she and Mama did not need his constant presence. They did not even need Albert's wife to make a home for Mama while Nellie was away on out-of-town assignments.

Mama was about to have her own home, and a very splendid one. Nellie was having it specially built for her on Marlborough Road in Brooklyn. It was a miniature Dutch castle, impressive outside and elegantly furnished within. For companionship Mama had the devoted Mrs. Daniels, who had kept her company while Nellie went around the world. The brothers and their families would be most welcome whenever they cared to visit. But it was Mama's home and would remain so.

The new house was finished by autumn, and Mrs. Cochrane and her companion moved in. For the next few years the house was more a base than a home for Nellie, a place to come to and depart from.

Her editor had predicted that the time would come when the public had had enough of Nellie Bly. There he reckoned without Nellie herself. She was not content to rest on her fame as the first girl to go around the world. She was first and last a reporter. Now that she was nationally known, she could take the whole country for her field.

Before six months had passed, she was back at the *World* office with a new proposal.

"I'll go wherever things are happening," she told her editor. "If the *World* wants to print what I see, that's fine. If not, I'll sell my articles to local papers. I've had plenty of offers. But the *World* will always be my first choice."

"You're a loyal girl, Nellie," Mr. Chambers approved. "And a smart one. Of course we'll want whatever you find that interests our readers. But that needn't keep you from selling to out-of-town papers as well. What you want is a syndicate arrangement. One leading paper in each community to carry the story. Bill Nye does that with his humorous articles. You'd better talk to him."

Nellie talked to Nye, the famous humorist whose articles often shared the Sunday supplement with hers. They worked out a syndicate contract to be offered to newspapers all over the country. Each paper agreed to take a certain number of articles a year, choosing those that would appeal to their readers in their particular cities.

This was newspaper work as Nellie had not dared to hope it could be. She was free of any editorial dictation. She ranged the country, finding her stories and writing them as she pleased. She covered the trial of a bomb-throwing anarchist and of a pathetic farm wife falsely accused of poisoning her husband. She was on hand for the Chicago railroad strike and for Coxey's unemployment march on Washington.

Her sympathies were always with the underdog, the ignorant and oppressed. She saw a strike from the workers' side, and slum housing as the tenants saw it. Greedy employers and indifferent landlords felt the sharp lash of her scorn. But she had a passionate faith in an aroused public opinion. People are good at heart, she maintained. Let them *know*. Show them the evil, and they will wipe it out. That was her idea of what a newspaper reporter is for.

12 *The Ending Is Sad*

Nellie Bly was the country's best-known and most-loved reporter when she gave up newspaper work five years after her famous tour.

Her closest friends knew that she had been seeing a great deal of Robert L. Seaman, a Brooklyn manufacturer more than twice her age. They had no idea that she intended to marry him until the wedding invitations came in the mail.

Nellie's busy life had left her little time for romance. She had plenty of suitors, but she took none of them seriously. Perhaps she had heard too much in her youth about the necessity of finding a husband. She must have taken satisfaction in proving how well a girl can do without one.

She first met Robert Seaman at a businessmen's convention in Chicago. He told her about the improvements he was making in his kitchenware factory, and asked for her suggestions. She found that he was sincerely concerned for the comfort and welfare of his employees. Back in New York, she visited his factory and approved what she saw.

Apparently she approved of Mr. Seaman too. They were married in the summer of 1895, from the Brooklyn house. Nellie's mother was in failing health, so they took Mama to live with them in their new home on West 37th Street, New York. On Mrs. Cochrane's death a year or so later, Brother Albert managed to get his hands on the Brooklyn house, claiming that Mama had promised it to him.

Nellie could afford to let him have it. Her earnings, which had amounted to some twenty-five thousand dollars a year, were profitably invested. Her husband was a wealthy man.

With time and money to spare, she threw herself into charitable work. She worked tirelessly on the boards of rest shelters and orphanages, giving money where funds were needed. The hired managers of these places could not pull the wool over Nellie's eyes. She had seen the institutions from the inside, as one of the needy who were supposed to be helped. They were helped more effectively and generously under Nellie's sharp supervision.

The marriage was a happy one. Nellie and her husband made a leisurely trip abroad, covering in months the route she had skimmed over in days. They did a moderate amount of entertaining. When later Mr. Seaman's eyesight failed, Nellie became his right hand at the factory. Old employees still living speak gratefully of her thoughtful kindliness to them.

Robert Seaman died in 1910. Nellie continued the business on her own and did badly with it. The times were hard, and she was more interested in the welfare of her workers than in profits. The company was forced into bankruptcy. Nellie was left a childless, middle-aged widow, with just enough money to keep her in a second-rate hotel. If she wanted more, she would have to go back to newspaper work.

The ending to her story is a sad one. The newspaper world had moved on, leaving her behind. Girl reporters were accepted now, younger and prettier and better educated. There were new faces in editorial offices. No one needed a forgotten celebrity.

It was only for old time's sake that she was given a few assignments. Arthur Brisbane of the *Journal* let her do some sob stories on the plight of homeless children. He sent her up to Sing Sing to witness an execution and denounce capital punishment. In the old days the death-chamber article would have created a sensation. Now it seemed that no one cared. The name of Nellie Bly, so long out of print, had lost its magic.

Elizabeth Cochrane Seaman, aged fifty-five, died at St. Mark's Hospital on January 27, 1922. Her death notices brought the magic name briefly into print again. Nowadays, if it lives at all, it lives because of her round-the-world trip. A newspaper stunt of no lasting value is remembered, and her services to humanity are forgotten.

Yes, Nellie Bly went around the world in less than eighty days. But she also got decent treatment for the insane, and heating stoves for sweatshop workers, and an end to dozens of evil rackets. If something must be forgotten, let it be the eighty-day junket. Nellie Bly has a nobler claim to our remembrance than that.